OLD
WIVES'
TALES
By Sue Castle

# *Contents*

# *Introduction*

On a news show the other morning, in response to one guest's remark, the host asked, "Is that true, or is it just another old wives' tale?" Why IS the received wisdom of the ages so often dismissed in such a cavalier manner? Are all old wives' tales automatically thought of as nonsense?

These questions – and my own tendency to pass along some flimsy advice – made me stop and think. I felt compelled to get to the bottom of it all. Are all old wives' tales just so much superstitious nonsense, or is there much more to them than that? Is there a grain of truth to any of them?

For centuries, the collective memories and wisdom of mothers and grandmothers kept the family safe, strong and healthy. Experience was the greatest teacher of all (another old wives' tale?) for people who didn't have today's 'experts' to rely on. They had to deal with the forces of nature in the best way they could. My own mother ("Don't read in dim light. You'll ruin your eyes!") wasn't wrong about a lot of things. So how was I to separate what was really useful from what might be total hogwash?

Well, today we do have some pretty well-informed experts, and I decided to turn to them and others in my search for not only what's true and what isn't, but also the story behind how these tales came about.

Join me now in a fact or fiction mission of some of the best known old wives' tales – plus some old sailors' tales, farmers' tales and carousers' tales, as well.

I hope you enjoy them as much as I have.

# *Don't Cross Your Eyes & Other Things You Shouldn't Do*

## *Don't Cross Your Eyes; They'll Get Stuck That Way.*

**NOT TRUE**

The thought of going through life cross-eyed was enough for me to stop this particular trick. For some reason, maybe because it gets a laugh or will scare your little brother, most kids love to cross their eyes.

Lucky for them, there's absolutely no truth to this warning. In fact, ophthalmologists point out that children who have the muscular control to bring the pupils to the inner corners are probably the least likely to have crossed eyes.

The medical term for any condition where one or both eyes are turned abnormally is *strabismus.* Worried parents are told by concerned friends, "just wait and he'll outgrow it." "Not true!" say specialists. When it comes to starting treatment, usually vision therapy, the earlier the better, for psychological as well as physical reasons. We all know that other children can be really awful when encountering even a mildly cross-eyed playmate.

## *Don't Put Plants and Flowers in a Sick Room. They Use Up Oxygen.*

**NOT TRUE**

Imagine this... you've got a cold. You are awakened in the middle of the night by the sound of someone or something breathing. In a panic, you leap out of bed, switch on the light, and find your houseplants inhaling in the corner of your room.

To hear the old wives' tales about it, you'd think that's exactly what happens if you're careless and allow these grasping, gasping, greedy greens to suck up vitally needed oxygen from your sickroom.

Although, at our home, we sleep with a number of plants and have never heard them panting in the dark – and could not find one mention of this warning in dozens of home health care books – we decided to check this one out with the New York Botanical Garden anyway. To our surprise, in talking to Maria Long at the New York Botanical Garden, we discovered that many people, in fact, call up to ask this very question. One woman told them she had just thrown out every plant in the house when she heard about all the oxygen they steal. Was such a rash act necessary?

Plants do require some oxygen, says Ms. Long, for the process of *photosynthesis* (the method of turning sunlight into food). Like animals, they burn energy all the time, but they only photosynthesize during the day. So even if they were to gulp oxygen by the tankload, they would not do it at night.

Fortunately, plants don't actually breathe – day or night. The photosynthesis process involves so little oxygen that it is insignificant in human terms. As Ms. Long points out, even another human being, sleeping in the same room, will not use up all the oxygen, or even enough to interfere with the breathing of another person in the same room. So how much oxygen could a plant – or even many plants – use? The answer is nothing even remotely significant.

As a matter of fact, not only is this old wives' tale blatantly false, it is actually the reverse that is true. Plants in the sick room can, indeed, be of some help. According to recent studies, plants aid in the elimination of many air pollutants, especially carbon monoxide.

So don't hesitate to invite a leafy green plant into your home. Not only are they perfectly harmless, but they can go a long way to cheering up a sick person's room. Just check to make sure he or she isn't allergic.

## *Don't Read in Dim Light; You'll Ruin Your Eyes.*

**NOT TRUE**

Since I was a diligent carrot eater, and still became near-sighted enough by age 14 to wear glasses, my mother found another explanation: reading under the covers by flashlight (necessitated by a 9:00 p.m. lights off curfew based on the dictum that "Children need to get enough sleep"... I'll deal with that one later).

I grew up hearing that I ruined my eyes by reading in dim light, although the flashlight was really quite bright.

I have a real aversion to bright lighting, so my children grew up living in a house with adequate but indirect lighting, dimmers, and very few lamps. Aside from the constant complaints that they couldn't see what they were eating, there's no proof it affected their eyes. One child has 20/20 vision, and the other wears glasses only for reading.

Experts support my stubbornly defended belief that this truly is just an old wives' tale, albeit a very popular one. The American Academy of Ophthalmology assures us, "Reading in dim light can no more harm the eyes than taking a photograph in dim light can harm the camera." The eye muscles that change the focus of the lens aren't 'hurt' by dim light; this is not the cause of nearsightedness or farsightedness.

However, the eye muscles might get tired if you have to strain to read, and that could cause tension headaches. Besides having adequate light, doctors recommend taking a break after every 20 minutes of reading. Just look up from your book and focus on something 15 to 20 feet away.

## *You'll Get Zits If You Eat Chocolate, Fried Food.*

**NOT TRUE**

The list could go on and on about all the things that cause pimples. An estimated 80 percent of adolescents suffer from zits or pimples at one time or another, so it's no wonder that so many theories appear.

The good news from dermatologists is that the above are just old wives' tales. In a study performed at Yale University School of Medicine, teens consumed large amounts of chocolate. Even those who were prone to acne did not show a significant difference. In fact, doctors say that there are no foods that cause pimples – unless you're allergic to a specific food, in which case the allergy shows up as a rash. Since adults can generally eat chocolate and fried foods without breaking out, this is obvious common sense.

Dermatologists also confirm that zits are not a result of sex, lack of sex or exercise. And there's no need to scrub the skin off your face in order to keep your pores clean... no matter what the ads recommend. Dirt and surface oil do not create zits, and a normal amount of washing with mild soap and water is usually adequate.

So what does cause pimples and acne? While the underlying cause is still unknown, genetics may play a role in determining the severity of this common condition. However, doctors do have a clear understanding of the process. Here is a simple explanation.

Hormones, particularly testosterone, increase during adolescence, stimulating the sebaceous glands to enlarge and produce more oil (sebum) in the skin's pores (follicles).

The pore is also lined with skin cells. Normally, the oil and dead skin cells that are shed by the lining rise to the surface and are washed away. A pimple is formed when the dead cells clog the opening to the pore, causing the cells, oil and bacteria to build up until the pore is infected.

Besides genetics, stress may also play a role in triggering the process that produces acne. This could provide the answer to the eternal question: "Why did I have to get this gigantic zit just before the prom!"

## *Eating Too Much Will Stretch Your Stomach. In Order to Lose Weight, You Have to Shrink Your Stomach.*

**NOT TRUE**

Millions of dieters believe these are valid explanations for how you gain weight in the first place (the larger your stomach, the more you need to eat) and how you begin to lose weight (you eat less when your stomach is small). Makes perfect sense, doesn't it?

It certainly did to me until I started doing research for this book. The doctor I checked with just laughed and explained that you can no more shrink your stomach by not eating than you can shrink your lips. The same goes for stretching it through overeating. Now, some desperate, obese people have had their stomachs stapled so that they can eat only small amounts. That works, but what a drastic way to lose weight.

There is a reason why these old wives' tales might seem true. When you eat smaller amounts at meals, your stomach produces less gastric acid, so it's less likely to rumble and you can go longer between meals without feeling hunger pangs.

My problem is whether to tell the truth to my husband. After all these years of laying a guilt trip over second helpings at the dinner table, I dare not lose my only strategy for helping him keep his diet.

## *Eating Too Much Sugar Can Cause Diabetes.*

**NOT TRUE**

It's true that sugar intake is a serious problem for diabetics. But according to the American Diabetes Association, the condition occurs when the body produces insufficient or inefficient amounts of insulin, which is the hormone that regulates how the body metabolizes sugar.

But sugar does not cause diabetes. What does? Diabetes tends to run in families, so there might be a genetic factor. Also, about 80 percent of people with adult onset diabetes are overweight, and obesity makes it more difficult for insulin to work efficiently.

## *If You Don't Stop Sucking Your Thumb, You'll Get Buck Teeth.*

**MAYBE**

Dentists say not to worry even if a child's first teeth do protrude from thumb-sucking. It won't affect the permanent teeth unless thumb-sucking continues when they start to come in, around age five to six. But most children have long since given up the practice by this age. If not, check with your child's doctor about the best way to break the habit.

Thumb-sucking is really a normal instinct. Sonograms show some babies even start in the womb. Psychologists advise this is a natural way of dealing with tension, boredom and fatigue. Too bad adults can't indulge!

## *Don't Go Out With Wet Hair; You'll Catch a Cold.*

**NOT TRUE**

There appears to be real logic behind this. After all, when you go out with wet hair, the hair begins to dry and the water evaporates. And what is evaporation? Right. A cooling process. So going out with wet hair will make your head colder. How does that open you up to the ravages of the cold germ? It lowers your resistance, you say. The same goes for...

Sitting in a Draft... or... Not Wearing a Hat... or... Not Wearing a Sweater... or... Getting Your Feet Wet... or... Getting Chilled... etc., etc.

This must be true. After all, think of all those movies where someone gets cold and wet, and in the next scene he's sitting with his feet in a tub of hot water and a thermometer in his mouth. People swear they can always put their finger on just such an event before each onslaught of cold or flu.

But, how many times have you become cold, gotten wet, been caught in a storm, been dumped overboard in a lake, shoveled snow, or become cold in a thousand other ways, and didn't catch cold? How many incidents of sudden chill have you breezed through in perfect health?

The Common Cold Unit in Salisbury, England, conducted repeated experiments in which people were left shivering in the cold, and did not come down with any more colds than those

who stayed warm. Studies done in Texas went one step further. Actual viruses were dropped into the subjects' noses, but exposure to low temperature made no difference as to frequency or severity of colds.

Still unconvinced? Let's look at what modern medicine does know about the common cold. First of all, with over 200 viruses, there's no such thing as a 'common' cold. Next, there is only one way to catch a cold – by coming into contact with a cold virus. The good news is once you've had a cold, you're immune to that particular virus. This explains why children generally catch more colds than adults. However, there is no clear explanation for why some people show more resistance to cold viruses than others, who seem to pick up everything 'going around'.

But why do you tend to get more colds in the winter when you're more likely to get chilled? The answer is simply that that is when you spend more time indoors, in closer contact with people and their germs. Even in warm climates, children are in school during the winter months, so they pick up cold viruses and then bring them home.

How are these viruses passed from one person to another? Of course, everyone is aware of the dangers of coughing and sneezing, but new studies show that finger-to-nose contact is the most likely means of transmission. Doctors say the best way to avoid colds is to keep your hands clean, and keep them away from your nose.

## *Don't Go Swimming Right After Eating; You'll Get Cramps and Drown.*

**NOT TRUE**

If there is one rule that has caused more childhood misery than this one, I can't imagine what it would be. I thought my parents were bad when they made me sit on the beach for at least an hour, sweltering in the hot sun, hands sticky with the juice of tomatoes or oranges combined with sand, and gazing longingly at the relief of cool clear water just yards away. But a friend of mine who grew up in Cuba tells us the required wait was three hours in her family. That meant she had to eat breakfast at six in the morning if she wanted to go swimming with her friends.

The reasoning given by parents went something like this: The blood supply the muscles would normally use for swimming is needed to digest the food. Therefore, the resulting lack of oxygen would increase the tendency for muscles to cramp.

By the time our own children were of swimming age the waiting period had been modified down to a half hour or less. But the concern was still about cramps after eating.

Did all that misery really save lives, or did generations of children suffer in vain?

To find out, we went to the source of all good information about swimming: The American Red Cross.

Bev Hoover, Health and Safety Specialist at the national office, told us that cramps can and do occur while swimming.

But they have little or nothing to do with how soon after eating you take the plunge. They occur, for the most part, in one of your muscles: either in your arm or your calf. These cramps can be caused by fatigue, cold, overexertion, or simply by being out of shape.

Stomach cramps, which are better defined as abdominal or gastrointestinal cramps, can result from the same factors. More likely, they can be attributed to overeating, or eating food that may have spoiled from the heat. But these cramps will appear whether or not you go swimming.

The important thing to know is what to do when you get a cramp. The Red Cross says: Just relax, do not become panicky or alarmed. Reassure yourself that your buoyancy hasn't changed, and you are still floating. Often just changing your swimming stroke will relieve the cramp. Or float while massaging the muscle. If it's a foot cramp and you're in deep water, take a deep breath, roll face down, extend your leg and flex it, and reach down and massage the muscle.

Often an intestinal cramp will pass in a few moments, especially if you don't get anxious. If it doesn't pass, then get out of the water as soon as possible, again without panic.

Whenever you're at the beach or pool, remember the American Red Cross's 'dangerous toos' – too tired, too cold, too far from safety, too much sun, and too much hard playing. But going swimming 'too soon' after eating isn't included. If your kids, or you for that matter, want to plunge into the water right after a hot, sticky lunch, it's fine. Let's finally leave this OWT high and dry on the beach.

## *Shaving Makes Your Hair, or Beard, Grow Back Thicker.*

**NOT TRUE**

I wonder if the reason European women tend to avoid shaving their leg and underarm hair is the fear that if they do, the hair will grow in thicker.

I still remember the agonizing that went on at teen sleepovers as we struggled with the momentous decision: Did we really need to start shaving our legs, or could we hold off a little longer? We never doubted that the hair would grow in thicker and make us slaves to the razor for the rest of our lives. What we didn't know, my husband pointed out, was that teenage boys have a similar fear.

They're not worried about their legs, of course, and they have an almost suicidal urge to get on with the business of scraping their faces – which has become a modern rite of manhood. But they do worry about shaving too high up on their cheeks, thinking, as we do, that the facial hair is going to start sprouting where it's going to be . . . ooooh, gross!

Well, we can all relax, and shave to our hearts' content.

In *The Skin Book*, dermatologists Arnold Klein and James Steinberg give the reassuring news that there is no truth whatsoever in this commonly held belief. Shaving an area will not make the hair grow back thicker. This really is just an old wives' tale.

They also have something to say about another shibboleth of shaving . . .

## *Shaving Against the Grain Will Make Your Hair Tougher.*

**NOT TRUE**

During our research we discovered why it was that men began to shave their faces in the first place. Contrary to the popular wisdom that men shave to make themselves more handsome, it seems the practice dates back to the days of hand-to-hand combat. Men shaved their beards because they didn't want to give the enemy any more to grab onto than they already had.

If we must shave, and I refer to men and women both, it is advisable to shave 'with the grain'. Not, however, because it will make the hair or beard tougher, but because it will prevent ingrown hairs.

Hairs don't grow straight out from the skin, but rather at an angle ranging from 30 to 60 degrees. If the hair gets cut 'against the grain', or against this angle, it is left with a sharp point which can pierce the skin or grow back into the follicle as it curls back. Because of this problem, it is also not a good idea to shave too closely. Interestingly, this is more of a problem for African American men because of their naturally curly hair, which can too easily curl back into the follicle.

Drs. Klein and Steinberg offer this simple, surefire strategy for men who have a problem with ingrown facial hairs: "Grow a beard." Then just make sure you don't get into any hand-to-hand combat.

## *Don't Touch Poison Ivy Blisters, You'll Spread Them.*

**NOT TRUE**

Poison ivy has been tormenting people for centuries. There it is, lurking in the brush, waiting to smear the unsuspecting and afflict them with an itchy, pimply, blistery, fast-spreading rash. We're warned to watch out for "three leaves on a red stem"... a description that happens to fit lots of greenery. So it's tough to avoid it until it's too late, and recognition usually hits when the itchy blisters appear. The reflex is to scratch, and the last thing you want to hear is that you'll only keep spreading them.

Well, there's good news and bad news. The good news is that you can't spread poison ivy by touching (or even breaking) the blisters – assuming you've washed the area so there's no plant resin left on the skin. The belief that poison ivy spreads through the bloodstream is equally false. The bad news: It's still not a good idea to scratch, since broken skin can become infected, making things even worse.

So why do blisters often continue to appear on different parts of the body for days, even weeks after the first signs? First, there's the strong probability that it wasn't just your skin that came in contact with the plant; it was also your clothing, shoes, gardening tools, etc. Second, if it isn't washed off, the oil or resin from the plant can last almost indefinitely at full strength. Since you may be unaware you've encountered poison ivy (it takes two to four days for the first red spots or blisters to show), the resin could have been spread to everything you've touched. Finally, the spots that appear later may have received a lighter brush with the plant.

So, the question is, is there anything that can be done to stop the spread?

If you're lucky enough to recognize that you've just walked through a patch of poison ivy, wash the resin off immediately with soap and water or rubbing alcohol. This might prevent any reaction.

Then, as soon as is practical, strip and wash your clothing... don't forget to wipe off your shoes, too. Even after you've started to itch, wash everything you were wearing or might have touched – tools, steering wheels, etc. If you do all of this (or are sure you haven't been near anything green for weeks), but still break out, try washing the dog.

That's how to help stop the spread, but what helps relieve the itch? Doctors recommend using calamine lotion or cool compresses of witch hazel or Burow's solution. A mild hydrocortisone cream can also be applied on a small area if the skin isn't broken. Extremely sensitive people may need a shot of corticosteroids.

All this advice also holds true for poison oak and poison sumac.

## *Turning a Light Off Just for a Few Minutes Uses Up More Energy Than It Saves.*

**NOT TRUE**

I readily admit that I did not inherit this belief from my mother. Whenever she visits me, or more importantly, when we visit her, she always comments on my family's habit of leaving the lights on all over the house. She refused to buy my explanation (even though I started out in college as a physics major) that it uses up energy to keep turning lights on and off. After checking with our public power company, Con Edison, I found my mother is absolutely right... this is just another OWT! Flipping a switch simply breaks (Off) or completes (On) an electrical circuit, and does not use any energy, electrical, that is. Of course, it still requires human energy to flip the switch.

If that's the problem around your house (and it does take time to break habits), Con Ed points out that at 13.2 cents per kwh (kilowatt-hour), a 100-watt bulb costs 1.3 cents per hour of use. This may not seem like very much, but it sure adds up by the time the bill comes.

## *Use White Wine to Remove Red Wine Stains.*

**NOT TRUE**

With all the recent publicity about the benefits of red wine, health-conscious Americans have started drinking more red wine at dinner – with the inevitable result. Last week, I watched skeptically as a friend used white wine to remove red wine stains from a valuable antique linen tablecloth. She had heard 'somewhere' that it really worked, and the spots did seem to be lighter. But after the area dried, there were new, even larger, blotches from the white wine. No question, this is a real OWT.

Professor Herb Barndt, of the Philadelphia College of Textiles and Science, classifies all wines as causing the same type of stain since they all contain alcohol, fruit and sugar. In his handy book *How to Remove Spots and Stains*, Professor Barndt recommends the following method for wine removal (test first on an inconspicuous area for color loss or damage):

"Sponge off stain with cool water. For washable fabrics, stretch the stained area over a bowl, pour salt over the stain, and pour boiling water through the fabric from a height of 12 inches. If the fabric can't take boiling water, pour salt on the stain and moisten. Let stand, then scrape the salt off and rinse. If these methods are too harsh for the fabric or it is non-washable, use an oil solvent. If any stain remains, apply a vinegar solution (half water) and rinse."

The use of salt and cool water does seem to support the more common notion that Club Soda Removes Wine Stains. This certainly is more practical as immediate first aid during a dinner party than the boiling water procedure. But be sure to use club soda, not seltzer, since the latter is usually salt free.

And here are two final axioms from Professor Barndt that are worth remembering...

Never Use Heat on a Sugar Stain!

Never Use Soap on – and Never Iron – a Fruit Stain!

# *Feed a Cold, Starve a Fever & Other Miracle Cures*

## *Feed a Cold, Starve a Fever.*

**NOT TRUE**

Here's another OWT that is so ingrained that we don't even question it. But there's one problem, a problem that surfaced again as we asked a doctor for some medical backup.

The doctor began talking about feeding colds and starving fevers when he stopped, scratched his head and said, "Or is it 'Feed a fever and starve a cold'?"

Anyway, he went on to say it really doesn't matter, since neither one is true. If you need one simple answer, it should probably be 'drown 'em both', because both colds and fevers are helped by liquids. Fever is a condition that dehydrates the body, and therefore fluids should usually be ingested.

In addition, the advice is that when a person has a cold, and is hungry, by all means he or she should eat. If you go along with most of the medical community, which now acknowledges some benefit from vitamin C, then you should especially eat and drink those fruits and vegetables that are high in vitamin C. Your body can also use the energy supplied by a well-balanced diet.

So the dictum should be . . . Feed a Cold, Feed a Fever!

## *Chicken Soup Is the Best Medicine for a Cold.*

**MAYBE**

A sense of great awe comes over me as I approach this old wives' tale. I mean, who am I to comment on one of the universal truths of the ages? But, like the proverbial fool, it is my sworn duty to rush in, even to a place where angels utter not a peep.

I could 'chicken' out of this whole challenge by taking refuge behind the one statement about this 'Jewish penicillin' that nobody would ever argue with: "It couldn't hurt."

The obvious benefit, when you have read all that is written about treating colds and flu, is that it's the hot liquid characteristic of chicken soup that makes it effective. Colds and fevers tend to dehydrate the body, and cause chills; therefore hot liquids help.

Picky appetites can also be tempted by the aroma and flavor of chicken soup, especially when homemade. Even with the fat skimmed off (current recommendation) it delivers protein, carbohydrates, some vitamins and other helpful nutrients in an easily digested form. This makes it an excellent 'first food' during illness.

So far so good.

However, like prunes, chicken soup has other qualities, chemical compounds, or whatever you want to call it, that do, indeed, make it a very effective treatment for colds, flu and similar ailments.

Where else but in Miami Beach could the scientific principals behind chicken soup be better explored? A study made at the Mt. Sinai Medical Center found that hot chicken soup, either the smell or the taste, "appears to possess an additional substance for increasing the flow of nasal mucus." This helps remove germs from your system and gets you on the way to a speedy recovery.

## *An Apple a Day Keeps the Doctor Away.*

**NOT TRUE**

For starters, this statement is misleading. These days, nobody has to keep a doctor away – they never come. Doctors don't make house calls. The correct phrasing of this should be 'An Apple a Day Keeps You Away From the Doctor.'

But, does any rational person actually believe that apples keep you healthy? Well, maybe, but with a whole bunch of qualifiers.

For instance: 'An Apple a Day Will Keep You From Getting the Little Annoying Everyday Sicknesses Like Flu or the Common Cold.'

Well, the Nobel Prize-winning Dr. Linus Pauling promoted the idea that high amounts of vitamin C can prevent colds, and the controversy over this has been raging ever since. But where does the apple stand in relation to other fruits in the delivery of vitamin C? By comparison to citrus foods – oranges, grapefruits and lemons – apples do not come out too high. In fact, nutritionists rank cantaloupe, guava, papaya, berries, broccoli, green pepper, tomatoes, spinach, collard greens, potatoes, asparagus and parsley above apples as a rich source of vitamin C.

OK, let's try fiber. After all, we could say that 'An Apple a Day Will Keep Constipation Away'. There's no question that doctors and nutritionists all strongly recommend a good daily intake of dietary fiber – especially from fruits, vegetables, nuts and seeds – as the sure path to regularity. Research also indicates that fiber may help in preventing colon cancer, diabetes and heart disease.

But once again, the apple trails behind the pack. The American Health Association rates baked beans, wheat germ, kidney beans, navy beans, lima beans and bran-rich cereal higher than the apple. Although, when eaten with the skin, it is considered as good a source of fiber as other fruits.

When it comes to more serious disease, such as cancer, there is absolutely no indication that apples are at all beneficial. What has made recent headlines is BROCCOLI! Studies over the past few years have statistically shown that people who eat regular, moderate amounts of cruciferous vegetables have a lower incidence of certain types of cancer. Now, researchers at Johns Hopkins School of Medicine have isolated a specific chemical in broccoli, called sulforaphane, that causes a significant increase in some of the body's protective enzymes that help guard against malignancies. Both microwaving and steaming methods of cooking leave the chemical intact.

So it's . . . 'Broccoli Every Day May Keep Cancer Away.'

The bad news for those who simply can't stand broccoli is that there are no plans to produce the chemical in pill form for painless consumption. The good news? Other cruciferous vegetables, including brussels sprouts, cauliflower and kale, as well as some noncruciferous ones, like carrots, also contain high concentrations of sulforaphane.

In 'Meals That Heal', a segment on CBS News, some other foods received attention as having possible benefits for a variety of conditions. Cherries and raspberries were highlighted for osteoporosis; grapefruit, oranges and, yes – broccoli – for relieving arthritis pain; bananas for decreasing blood pressure when under stress; licorice for ulcers; and passion fruit for insomnia.

So we have to pity the poor apple. After all these years and all that glory, it appears to be a rather ineffective little fruit.

Perhaps the proverb should be, 'An Apple a Day Makes a Delicious Non-Fattening Snack, and You Get Some Fiber, a Little vitamin C, and potassium In the Bargain.' By the way, biting into an apple also helps clean your teeth – so we can also say, 'An Apple a Day Keeps the Dentist Away!'

## *Milk Is Good for an Ulcer.*

**NOT TRUE**

This one is so entrenched in the media, it's become a cliche... someone at the bar says, with a grimace, "Just gimme a glass of milk." And everyone knows he's nursing an ulcer, is probably anxious, uptight, etc. With just that one line, a writer can convey a complete personality.

Until fairly recently, generations of people suffering the pain of gastric ulcers were advised, even by doctors, to regularly drink milk as part of the treatment. It seemed to make sense since, after all, milk could be digested by infants and certainly wasn't spicy. However, research has now shown that, instead of soothing an ulcer, milk actually aggravates the condition.

An ulcer occurs in the stomach or duodenum when acid secretion wears away an area of the protective mucous lining. Milk, while it may seem to be a bland food, actually stimulates the production of gastric acid... which only increases the irritation and pain. Other culprits creating excessive acid include stress, smoking, caffeine, alcohol, poor nutrition, lack of sleep and the use of some medications, like aspirin.

A bland diet may help relieve the symptoms during an acute attack, but it doesn't heal an ulcer... or prevent one from occurring. The good news... new research at the Baylor College of Medicine in Houston indicates that nearly all ulcers are caused by a common bacteria, *Helicobacter pylori*. In their study, taking a combination of two common antibiotics (to kill the bacteria), an ulcer drug and over-the-counter medication for an upset stomach, did more than just heal the ulcers. Ninety-five percent of patients with gastric ulcers had no recurrence in the next two years. So if you're one of the 10 million Americans who suffer from ulcers, check with your doctor.

## *Put Butter on a Burn Right Away.*

**NOT TRUE**

Once again, the wisdom of the ages can be a dangerous thing. Rubbing butter, oil or ointment immediately on a burn only helps to keep the heat in and increases the damage to tissue and blood vessels. Later on as it's beginning to heal, for a minor burn, it's fine to use bacitracin ointment, juice from an aloe vera leaf or vitamin E oil.

The first thing you should do is to cool the area. Remember, even if the skin looks only a little red, burns are usually worse than they first appear because the heat is still penetrating below the surface of the skin.

Here's what the experts say to do immediately for scalds and flame burns.

**1.** If the burned area is covered with clothing, first pour cool water on the burn, then remove the soaked or scorched clothing, unless it's stuck to the skin.

**2.** Immerse the area in cool water or apply cool wet compresses for 10 to 15 minutes. If the compresses get warm, pour cold water over them. Never put ice directly on the skin because it can cause further damage.

**3.** If the injured area is larger than a half inch, or the burn has destroyed the skin, call your doctor.

**4.** In cases of extensive burns, after cooling the areas, wrap the victim in a clean sheet, then a blanket to prevent losing body heat. Get help or go to an emergency room at once.

A few weeks ago, a friend sadly told me that his 15-month-old grandson was severely scalded after tipping a cup of hot tea all over himself. Since they lived across the street from the hospital, they picked him up and rushed him over to the emergency room... a natural reaction. But even during that short time, the burning continued. I thought... if only they had immediately poured on cool water, stripped off his clothing, put him in a cool bath for a few minutes, and then gone to the hospital. Of course, this wasn't the time to say anything.

## *Never Take a Bath When You're Sick.*

**NOT TRUE**

Tell this one to my husband and you'll get an argument – and one of his famous war stories. Not a war story, actually it's more of a basic training story.

Having grown up 'sweating' out fevers, my husband had always believed that washing one's fevered frame with anything but alcohol meant instant death. So, when he found himself ill and feverish one night while he was in the Army, he made sure to work up a good sweat and slept in a soaking wet tent with soaking wet clothing. When he was sent to the post hospital, the army doctors immediately tossed him into a shower. With his initial shock worn off, and tucked snugly between clean sheets, he realized that, not only did he not die, but it was a lot more pleasant to be sick and clean than sick and smelly.

Since then, whenever he comes down with a flu or a bad cold, he may not always be the best patient, but he's definitely the cleanest, taking at least a couple of showers a day, especially when he has chills and fever.

It works for my husband, but what do doctors say? The answer is that baths and even shampoos are perfectly fine, for children, as well as adults. Not only does it make you feel better, but as you've read, it also helps lower a fever. Just be sure to dry off in a warm room.

## *You Can Cure Hiccups By:*

- *Swallowing a Teaspoon of Sugar.*
- *Blowing Into a Paper Bag.*
- *Being Surprised.*
- *Holding Your Breath for One Minute.*

**MAYBE**

We don't know how prehistoric man handled his hiccups, but there's no question he had them – people have been hiccuping since the dawn of creation. Now, through the wonders of ultrasound, we can even see the fetus hiccup inside the uterus. After all those years, one would think that doctors could have identified the cause and the cure.

Think again.

Hiccups remain a medical mystery. Experts believe that hiccups start when something disrupts the rhythmic movement of the diaphragm, a dome-shaped muscle that stretches between the lungs and the stomach. It contracts and pulls air into the lungs when you inhale, then relaxes and pushes air back out when you exhale. The most likely explanations given for the disruption are eating too much, which causes the enlarged stomach to press on the diaphragm, and taking in too much air, which thus disrupts regular breathing.

All this sounds reasonable as to how hiccups start, but what about stopping them? Over the centuries, there have been thousands of cures (in addition to the ones above) that people swear by. *The Journal of Clinical Gastroenterology* has even published the following list of suggestions:

- Yank forcefully on the tongue.
- Lift the uvula (that little flap at the back of your mouth) with a spoon. (Try not to gag!)
- Chew and swallow dry bread.
- Suck a lemon wedge soaked with Angostura bitters. (Yuck!)
- Compress the chest by pulling the knees up or leaning forward.
- Hold your breath for one minute.

The general idea is to overwhelm the nerve impulses that cause the hiccuping (maybe that's why being surprised might help), or to increase the carbon dioxide levels in the blood (the logic behind blowing into a paper bag). My favorite remedy – drinking water from the opposite side of a glass – doesn't seem to fit either category. However, as one doctor has pointed out, "Anytime you have lots of ways to treat something it means that none of them works very well; otherwise, there would be only one way to treat it."

The bottom line is to use whatever works for you. Fortunately, most hiccups will stop on their own within a few minutes, even if you ignore them. But then there's poor Charles Osborne (1894-1990). He led a normal life, married twice and fathered eight children. His main problem was keeping his false teeth in place. He holds the Guinness World record for hiccups: 69 years, until his death.

## *Never Squeeze a Boil.*

**TRUE**

I sometimes wonder if, in the annals of psychotic behavior, there isn't a big fat file on people who like to squeeze boils. We've all met them. Upon sighting a boil, a strange glaze crosses their eyes, their forefingers extend into a pincer-like shape and they advance upon the boil like a predatory beast.

It's important to be able to impart the latest medical advice: The best way to handle a boil is to apply a warm compress and wait for it to 'come to a head'. It may be less satisfying and more time-consuming, but it lessens the chance of the various complications squeezing can bring about.

But first, what exactly is a boil?

A boil is formed when bacteria, called *staphylococcus*, gets into the skin and infects a blocked oil gland or hair follicle. This triggers a defense reaction in the body and white blood cells are rallied to the area. The ensuing conflagration produces pus, which raises the skin in a red, angry boil. And therein lies the danger of squeezing.

If the boil has not come to a head (a white or yellowish area at the peak of the swelling), squeezing can force the bacteria into the bloodstream, and possibly into the lymph system. If the infection travels to the brain, or if the person is nursing or diabetic, it can be very dangerous. Fever, chills or swellings of lymph nodes are signs that this spreading has occurred.

Warm compresses applied every few hours will bring the boil to a head in a few days. Or the body may simply reabsorb it. As a small boil comes to a head, and there is no sign of spreading infection, it is OK to lance it with a sterilized needle. Once the boil is draining, it's best to keep up the warm compresses and keep the area clean.

## *The Best Way To Stop a Nosebleed Is To:*

- *Put a Wad of Paper Under Your Lip.*
- *Put Ice on the Back of Your Neck.*
- *Tip Your Head Back.*

**NOT TRUE**

My husband, who played football in the days before face protectors and is therefore very familiar with bloody noses, swears by the wad of cloth or paper under the lip... he was back in the game within seconds. Besides sports injuries, nosebleeds can be caused by minor things, such as picking, blowing your nose too hard (or too often), excessive sneezing or coughing, and, in some cases, very dry air.

Dr. Henry Heimlich (of 'maneuver' fame) says that most of these minor bleeding episodes will stop shortly, even if left alone. He also advises applying pressure at the bleeding site by pressing the outside of the nostril toward the middle of the nose against the bony cartilage there. This pressure should be maintained for three minutes or longer, until the blood clots. That means no peeking to see if it has stopped.

Ice packs or cold compresses are advisable if the bleeding doesn't stop, but Dr. Heimlich says to put the compress or pack on the face, above the nose or right on the bridge of the nose, not at the back of the neck.

Tilting the head back is another OWT without basis. This makes the blood run down the throat and into the lungs, hiding the fact that the blood flow is continuing. The victim should actually be kept sitting upright, with the head in a normal position so the blood flows out of the nose, instead of down the throat.

If the flow does not stop, and especially if the blood is bright red and profuse – which could indicate arterial bleeding – keep the pressure on and rush the victim to a medical emergency facility or doctor. If nosebleeds are persistent or recurring, especially in the very young and the older adult, a doctor should be consulted.

Does the wad of paper work? It's supposed to apply pressure to the blood vessels in the nose, so that the flow stops and the blood can clot. But pinching the nose with two fingers is really more effective. However, my husband points out the former was more practical. After all, in those days a bloody nose wasn't enough to keep a player out of the game, and the wad under the lip kept the hands free to play football. Did it really stop the bleeding? Who knew? Who cared? The important thing was, who won?

## *Put a Steak on a Black Eye.*

**TRUE**

Remember how in cartoons and comic books they always showed the character, a split second after receiving a punch, with a large fresh steak on his eye? This habit more than likely got its start when steak was 25 cents a pound. But then again, nobody says you can't rub a steak with barbecue sauce and broil it after it's been used on a shiner.

My husband vividly remembers that his first black eye came at the hands of a kid named Wilfred. He was left with a steak on his eye and a constant reminder from his mother about how much it cost.

We asked Dr. John Seeder, an ophthalmologist practicing in New York City (where black eyes are not at all uncommon) for advice. He pointed out that a black eye was simply a bruise – just like a black-and-blue mark, with broken blood vessels and swelling. The best treatment for a bruise is an immediate application of anything cold, preferably something with a bit of flexibility that can conform to the contours of the face. Applying something cold works in two ways: It keeps the swelling down, and it helps stop the internal bleeding (the source of that mottled coloring) by constricting the broken blood vessels.

Think about it. In 1950, what could you count on to be cold, flexible and immediately available? Right! A piece of meat from the fridge. Cold compresses were too slow (remember those plastic sleeves filled with ice cubes? Ugh!), and rags soaked with cold water held their temperature for about two minutes. Plus, the curved ends of a steak fit so comfortably over the abused socket!

Doctors advise you not to take aspirin or blow your nose. Aspirin acts as an anticoagulant and slows the blood clotting. And, if the blow was pretty severe, there could be minor fractures of the eye socket, so blowing one's nose is another no-no. It can force air into the area and cause increased swelling.

## *Bed Rest Is Best for a Backache.*

**NOT TRUE**

Almost everyone is familiar with backaches. The American Academy of Orthopedic Surgeons rates back pain second to the cold for causing employees to miss work. According to most studies, four out of five people suffer a form of this affliction at some point in their lives.

Our pain began – when else? – with prehistoric man. The problem started when man stopped walking on all fours and began walking upright on his hind legs. Without the spine changing in some structural way to support the upright position, man didn't have a chance of a happy life walking on two feet. It's cold comfort to know we all start out with the same slight handicap.

The universal prescription for an aching back has always been bed rest, sometimes supplemented by traction devices and strong muscle-relaxing medications. Staying horizontal seems to make sense and usually helps relieve the pain . . . until you stand up. Then a cycle of chronic pain begins.

Recently, however, doctors have discovered that bed rest may actually be harmful. With prolonged bed rest there is a significant loss of muscle strength and tone, as well as loss of calcium from the bones. Even if you're in pain, inactivity can be more harmful than exercise. A reconditioning program which offers special workouts was developed by researchers at the University of Texas Southwest Medical Center in Dallas. Their program permanently returns nearly nine out of 10 workers with back injuries to their jobs. That's more than twice the results produced by traditional treatments of prolonged rest.

Instead of popping painkillers and taking to your bed, ask your doctor about a comprehensive program of physical exercises, muscle strengthening and stress reduction.

## *Knock on the Head? Stay Awake to Prevent a Concussion.*

**NOT TRUE**

In grade school, I was swung headfirst into the iron post of a 'maypole' . . . no wonder they've disappeared from modern playgrounds. After the crash I started walking home, began to feel very dizzy, and passed out with my first concussion. Had someone been around to get me up right away, could the concussion have been prevented? Not really.

Jeffrey Brown, M.D., writes, "Some parents mistakenly believe that keeping the child awake after a head injury will prevent a concussion." If a child has been crying and is exhausted, many pediatricians say it's all right to allow him to sleep for up to half an hour. The purpose of waking him up is to make sure he is arousable. If the injury occurs at night, the recommendation is to wake him up at least twice. But when there's a sudden loss of consciousness, like I had, it's important to get to the doctor immediately. This holds true for adults, as well as children.

## *Upset Tummy? Eat Crackers, Drink Flat Ginger Ale or Coke, Eat Ginger.*

**TRUE**

Not too long ago, one of the hazards of world travel was the inevitable stomach upset that kept you on a short leash to la toilette. Call it the water, the fatigue, the difference in time, the unfamiliar foods, a touch of motion sickness or a little of everything. Whatever the problem, you usually get an earful of advice in the form of local OWTs from hotel managers, chambermaids and assorted fellow travelers.

Sometimes, such advice actually proves helpful and you can discover local remedies that may work wonders. In France, the best one I learned of was an aperitif called Fernet Branca. It was one of the most bitter, worst-tasting fluids I have ever tasted – but it's nothing short of a miracle.

In America we have our own set of OWT cures that we can recommend to queasy foreigners: the most familiar being ginger ale or Coca-Cola, drunk after they have gone flat. We also have heard that eating dry crackers, like soda crackers, is an effective ploy. But do they really work?

Before continuing with the answer, let's first explore the differences in the kinds of upset stomach. Some upset stomachs appear around Thanksgiving and Christmas, the kind we get from food and alcohol overindulgence. But another common cause, experienced particularly by travelers, is motion sickness – *mal de mer* – which can happen on land and in the air, as well as at sea. This is caused by a whole series of confusing messages from the brain to the stomach and can interfere with the normal actions of the digestive system. These messages may be triggered by the eyes, the ears, or the brain in a variety of scenarios that we won't get in to here.

Although the triggering action for upset stomachs may differ between those caused by overindulgence and those caused by brain messages, the effect is similar: acids form, causing nausea and vomiting.

The question, then, is can we turn to OWTs for, if not a cure, then some relief?

Ginger really is a proven remedy for motion sickness. Made from a root, this spice has been used for centuries by ocean travelers, and recently passed muster in a series of scientific evaluations. In one test, it was found that two powdered ginger root capsules were more effective than an over-the-counter medication in preventing motion sickness.

According to the people at the Travelers Health Care Center at the University Hospitals of Cleveland, ginger works for stomach upset by absorbing acids in the gastrointestinal tract and thereby reducing nausea. Some sailing friends swear by fresh ginger, but others say it causes indigestion and heartburn. We can't tell you how much ginger is contained in the various ginger ales on the market, but it seems to help minor upsets: The liquid is also of value for the dehydration that usually accompanies stomach upset and vomiting. You drink it flat because the gas from carbonation is undesirable for an upset stomach.

Although the Coca-Cola base syrup is supposed to be a well-guarded secret, it is probably based on a common stomach remedy of the last century. A very close relative of this formula, called Unterberg, is known to German-Americans, who buy it in their ethnic delicatessens. Like Fernet Branca, this pretty foul-tasting syrup has been a dependable stomach remedy for many years.

These cola syrups are effective in most cases after the sickness has begun. They don't cure it, but they do provide some relief. The recommendation about drinking ginger ale flat also goes for Coke, although some people find that the burping action from the carbonation offers some relief from nausea.

Plain soda crackers – another common remedy – have two pluses. First, they are easily digestible and bland, and can absorb some of the offending fluids in your stomach. Second, they contain bicarbonate of soda and cream of tartar, which help neutralize acids. They're also easy to carry around. We always keep some on our sailboat.

Just in passing...much of the research material we have read on this subject says that motion sickness comes on rapidly. Our experience with sailing guests indicates there are some forewarnings to seasickness: One of these is yawning, followed by drowsiness. If the drowsy person is fed some Coca-Cola and crackers, or a ginger capsule at this stage – combined with heading for calmer waters – they may escape the nausea. Avoiding an upset stomach, on other occasions, usually requires sidestepping that extra helping.

## *You Can Sweat Out a Cold.*

**NOT TRUE**

What about the notion that heavy sweating and opening up your pores to get rid of all kinds of toxins will actually 'sweat out a cold'? The answer, once again from the esteemed doctors on the editorial board of the University of California's Berkeley Wellness Letter, is conveyed in just one word – "Nonsense!"

## *Wearing a Clove of Garlic Around Your Neck Will Keep You From Getting Sick.*

**NOT TRUE**

During the devastating Spanish flu epidemic of 1918, my mother recalls that she, along with her four siblings and parents, always wore fresh cloves of garlic, tucked in little bags, on a string around her neck. These peculiar necklaces have been thought – from as far back as the Middle Ages – to provide protection against catching coughs and colds.

It's true that the family did stay healthy, but the most likely explanation is that no sick person came near enough to spread the flu germ. Luckily, my mother did not believe strongly enough to perpetuate this particular old wives' tale during my school years.

Although wearing garlic may not have any practical value, eating garlic has been proven to be very beneficial... especially for the circulatory system. In controlled studies, large doses of garlic, given to healthy subjects for six months, significantly lowered blood cholesterol and triglyceride levels, and also raised the high density lipoproteins (HDLs or good cholesterol).

The results became even more impressive when patients with heart disease and elevated cholesterol levels ate the equivalent of one ounce of raw garlic a day. Garlic has been shown to help lower blood pressure in some people.

Less well-documented is the effectiveness of eating raw garlic to ward off colds and sore throats. But many people swear that it really works.

If you want to avoid the pitfalls of consuming raw garlic, but still reap the benefits, why not try microwaving an entire head. Just put it into a cup with a little liquid and 1 tablespoon of oil, cover tightly, cook for five minutes and let it stand for five minutes. It's easy and delicious!

## *Taking Large Amounts of Vitamin C Prevents Colds.*

**MAYBE**

The controversy on this one has been raging since the 1970s when Nobel scientist Dr. Linus Pauling published research on vitamin C. Various studies have either refuted or supported its usefulness, and entire books have been written on the subject. The latest medical thinking seems to be that it may work for some people to reduce the severity of symptoms.

For me, the bottom line is that, like chicken soup, it doesn't hurt, and may actually help. From personal experience, my husband and I have found that taking 1,500 mg of vitamin C every few hours, when we first feel symptoms coming on, often does stop a cold in its tracks. But not always!

The recommended daily intake of vitamin C is 250 mg, about the equivalent of seven servings of fruits and vegetables. Since smoking also reduces a person's level of vitamin C, the advice is to either stop smoking, eat more fruits and vegetables, or take a daily supplement.

## *Tonsils and Adenoids Cause Infections and Should Be Removed.*

**NOT TRUE**

Although I was only eight, I still clearly remember going into the hospital to have my tonsils and adenoids removed: the sweet sick smell of ether, counting backward until I went under, then waking up with a sharp pain in my throat. The up side was that I was allowed to eat all the ice cream I wanted. Sound familiar? This rather unpleasant experience was shared by most children as a result of the common belief, an 'old doctors' tale' that tonsils were the source of infections, especially if they were enlarged. Since children are likely to get frequent sore throats, it's worth sharing the latest medical thinking on the subject.

First of all, instead of causing infections, tonsils are there to help prevent infections from spreading. The purpose of these two masses of tissue at the back of the throat is to 'filter' germs from the throat. When bacteria or viruses occasionally infect this filter, the result is tonsillitis. Tonsils and adenoids also contain special cells that produce antibodies to help fight the bacteria and viruses.

As for their size, it's normal for tonsils to be enlarged in early childhood, and then begin to decrease around age six. Just because they're big, doesn't mean they have to come out. Adenoids serve much the same function as tonsils, but are less likely to become infected. However, they were often removed at the same time on the theory that 'as long as we're operating, why not'?

When is surgery recommended? The American Academy of Pediatrics gives only these five reasons:

1. history of abscesses
2. four or more episodes of tonsillitis in the past year
3. enlarged adenoids producing mouth breathing
4. hearing loss documented by audiogram
5. hypertension of the pulmonary artery

**While we're on the subject of sore throats, let's take a look at some of the more common remedies:**

## *Wrap a Scarf Around Your Neck.*

**NOT TRUE**

OK, it may not be so common here, but it's an old standby in Europe. Several years ago, we had a very sophisticated French girl visiting us for the summer. One day, she appeared for breakfast with a scarf wrapped several times around her neck. Since it was already 85 degrees Fahrenheit, I asked the natural question, "Why are you wearing a scarf?" Alex replied with obvious disdain for my ignorance, "I have a little sore throat, of course." Needless to say, this measure did very little to help her throat, but by the end of the day, she did have a serious case of prickly heat.

An Irish friend uses a scarf as a preventive measure whenever the temperature drops below 60 degrees Fahrenheit, and she swears that whenever she does get a sore throat, it's because she forgot her scarf.

I've shown her medical books stating clearly that sore throats are caused by viral infections, strep bacteria, irritation, even post nasal drip, but she'll never be convinced.

## *Drink Warm Milk With Honey and Whiskey.*

**NOT TRUE**

I shouldn't laugh at the scarf believers. When I was just out of college, I tried this remedy one night for a scratchy throat. The combination of Scotch, honey and milk was certainly soothing, but I may have gotten the proportions wrong because I woke up the next morning with a very sore throat... and a bad hangover.

Honey, though, has been revered for thousands of years as an all-purpose cure. The Koran calls it 'medicine for man'. Hippocrates, the father of modern medicine, praised honey: "It causes heat, cleans sores and ulcers, softens hard ulcers of the lips, heals carbuncles and running sores." The Egyptians, Hindus, Chinese, tribal Africans and medieval Europeans were just a few of the many other civilizations who used honey both inside and outside the body to treat various ailments.

It seems logical that the sugar in honey may be useful in relieving throat irritation. Since most sore throats are caused by viruses, and don't respond to antibiotics, the best bet is to treat the symptoms so the patient feels more comfortable. It certainly doesn't hurt to try.

Entire books have been devoted to folk remedies containing honey. But is there any scientific basis?

I haven't found any studies specifically made to determine the effectiveness of honey for sore throats. However, research has shown that sugar, the main ingredient in honey, is an antibacterial agent which can help prevent infections and speed healing (although antibiotic ointments are more effective).

## *Gargle With Warm Salt Water or Aspirin.*

**TRUE**

I was glad to learn this isn't just an OWT. Doctors often advise gargling every few hours with warm salt water (usually a teaspoon of salt to one glass) or two aspirin crushed in some water. Children should use acetaminophen or ibuprofen instead of aspirin because of the possible link to Reye's syndrome. Besides gargling (which not everyone can do easily), other recommendations for sore throat relief include:

- Drink plenty of liquids, especially hot ones like tea.
- Avoid acidic drinks that could increase irritation.
- Suck on hard candy or lozenges. The ones with mild anesthetics temporarily numb the pain, but sucking on anything will stimulate saliva and moisten the throat.
- Use a vaporizer in the room to help keep the air moist.

It's always a good idea to check with the doctor about the possibility of a strep infection, which can be treated best with antibiotics.

## *Hair of the Dog, the Ultimate Hangover Remedy.*

**NOT TRUE**

One of the funniest moments on the hit TV show *Northern Exposure*, was when Marilyn, the Native American secretary, offered a 'hair of the dog' to the very hungover Dr. Fleishman. He made a terrible face, spit it out and asked, "What was in that?" She replied, "Hair of the dog."

That was carrying things a bit far, because the expression is really 'the hair of the dog that bit you' and refers to giving the 'hungee' some of the same booze that did him in. We asked a number of people from the medical community and from the world of folklore about the origin of the expression, but the best explanation anyone could venture was that it comes from old England in her merry days.

Hangovers are really a terrible form of retribution for an evening of fun, much worse than we actually deserve. The worst part about them is there really isn't much that can be done except wait for the effects to wear off.

In researching cures for hangovers, we seemed to find as many different remedies as people asked. Which leads us to believe that nobody has a definitive answer. One thing is for sure, not one expert mentioned having another drink.

First, let's explain what being drunk is. Alcohol affects the brain when you have been drinking, and it gets there through the bloodstream. It also causes dehydration and depletion of vitamins like B, minerals like salt and potassium, and amino acids. But what causes the hangover?

A popular theory says the hangover is actually a withdrawal reaction. If that's the case, then the brain gets hooked on the alcohol in record time. According to Dr. Mack Mitchell of the Alcoholic Beverage Research Foundation, in just a few hours of drinking, the cells in the brain physically change. When the alcohol is all burned by the body and no more follows, these cells go into withdrawal. In addition, alcohol causes the blood vessels in the head to swell, and this, too, can be the cause of the headaches, dizzy spells and nausea.

Getting back to the 'hair of the dog', it would seem that if the withdrawal theory is valid, then some ingestion of alcohol would give some relief, and there are people who swear that it does. The only problem is that unless you are going to continually ingest alcohol, this solution only prolongs or postpones the inevitable hangover.

The most sensible thing is to understand that the hangover will run its natural course, and you will eventually recover. The idea, then, is to make life bearable, induce sleep if possible, and shorten the recovery time. If you remember how alcohol affects the body, it's easy to see how the various 'hangover remedies' have come into being.

One such remedy, a raw egg in tomato juice, more than likely provides a quick fix of proteins that house amino acids, while the tomato juice helps reverse the dehydration. Today, with salmonella rampant in raw eggs, you don't even want to think about this one.

The quickest route to recovery is eating a mild meal (no fat or fried food) and keeping it down. You'll be replacing everything the body has lost, and adding sugars, which burn away the alcohol faster. If you can only nibble and sip, then make sure you get fructose (honey or fruit juice), salt and potassium (bouillon or other soups are best), and carbohydrates (crackers, rice, potatoes), for the depleted amino acids. Drink lots of water, and take a painkiller such as ibuprofen or aspirin as you would for any headache. The old standby, an ice bag on the head, probably works by constricting swollen blood vessels.

Then there's coffee, drunk black and strong. Is there any benefit, or does it just give you the double whammy of a hangover and caffeine-jangled nerves? The fact is that coffee also aids in constricting those swollen blood vessels, and if taken in moderation (two cups), may reduce the headache.

Which leads us to another OWT...

## *Black Coffee Sobers You Up.*

**NOT TRUE**

This is one of the most common notions associated with drinking: If you can drink enough strong, black coffee, you'll sober up. It's often served at parties before people drive home, and offered free on New Year's Eve at highway stops. While it's true that caffeine may help relieve a hangover, and it may help a person stay awake, it does not lower the alcohol content in the body. So what you basically have is a wide awake drunk, still very dangerous behind the wheel. Better to drink a lot of fruit juice and wait until the sugar burns up enough alcohol.

## *Beer Before Whiskey, Pretty Risky; Whiskey Before Beer, Never Fear.*

**MAYBE**

This sounds a bit like one of those nautical rhyming tales, but we never found anything that traced it to the early sailors. The contribution, in fact, came from an old college friend who remembered this rhyme as a way to keep from getting sick at countless frat parties.

My husband said that, in the Army, there were many, many theories about what and how to drink without getting drunk. There are probably as many theories as there are ex-GIs. None of them seems to work very well. My neighbor, a chiropractor, swears by vitamin A. He believes he could drink all night without getting drunk if he stoked up on vitamin A first.

But, I digress.

Getting back to the optimum sequence of beer and whiskey, we checked with the Alcohol Research Foundation. No one there had even heard of it, but on purely physical grounds, the first reaction was that the theory was ridiculous. Alcohol is alcohol and it's the quantity that gets you drunk, not the order in which it is consumed.

But after thinking it over a minute, someone suggested there could be some benefit in drinking the whiskey first. One could drink beer after beer without feeling drunk, then have some whiskey, and end up with a dangerous amount of alcohol in the system.

But, if you started with whiskey, chances are you wouldn't have that many because the awareness of the alcohol content is so much stronger. Then, if you had a beer or two as chasers, the chances are you would not have consumed as much alcohol.

You might even get happy faster without actually consuming as much alcohol as you would have if you started with beer.

But it's only speculation, and I, for one, would never mix beer and whiskey, anyway. Red wine is my drink, because...

## *Red Wine Is Good for You.*

**TRUE**

For generations, the French have been the authorities, not only on making red wine, but drinking it. Besides being pleasurable to the palate, red wine is considered essential in maintaining good health and strength.

So it's not surprising that French researchers have taken a serious interest in determining if there was any scientific basis to the health claims for wine. Studies completed last year at the Hospital Cardiologic in Pessac reported that drinking red wine, did in fact, seem to significantly reduce the amount of 'bad' LDL (low-density lipoprotein) cholesterol – the kind that clogs arteries. At the same time, red wine increased the level of 'good' HDL (high-density lipoprotein) cholesterol – which may protect arteries by cleaning out fatty deposits. For those of you who prefer white wine, I'm sorry to convey the finding that it was only the red wine that had a beneficial effect on cholesterol levels.

A possible explanation came from additional research by plant scientists at Cornell's College of Agriculture and Life Sciences.

They succeeded in isolating a natural chemical in grapes, named *resveratrol*, which may be the critical substance. It's strongest in the grape skins, which are removed when making white wine. Interestingly, Japanese researchers have also identified resveratrol as the probable active ingredient in ancient remedies used for centuries in China and Japan to treat many different blood disorders. I recall that my mother-in-law was advised by her doctor (not Chinese) to drink a daily glass of red wine for her anemia, because it contained iron.

Last, there is also evidence that many red wines contain protein, which makes them food.

Now don't take all this good news about red wine as an excuse to sip your way through a bottle a day. Just because a little is good for you, doesn't mean a lot is better...moderation is the key word. And keep in mind that some medications shouldn't be mixed with alcohol in any amount, so always check with your doctor.

For those of you who can drink wine and would like to conduct your own study, it's worth noting that out of 30 wines tested by the Cornell researchers, red Bordeaux was found to contain by far the highest amounts of resveratrol.

This was the same type of wine used in the French study. *A votre sante!*

# *If You're Carrying High, It's a Boy & Other Expectations*

Until the last few hundred years or so, pregnancy and childbirth have been shrouded in awe and mystery. It's no wonder that countless old wives' tales were born and passed along for generations in an attempt at linking cause and effect. For example:

## *Predicting the Gender of the Baby.*

**NOT TRUE**

- If you carry high, it's a boy.
- If you carry low, it's a girl.
- Hold a needle on a thread above the abdomen: If it swings clockwise it's a boy; counterclockwise it's a girl.
- Hold a long piece of cotton over the abdomen: If the cotton moves back and forth, it's a boy; if it hangs straight, it's a girl.
- Compare the mother's age at time of conception with the year of conception: If both are even or odd, it will be a girl; If one is even and one is odd, it will be a boy.

And the list goes on and on. The last one dates back to the Aztecs, who were known to be advanced mathematicians. But not that advanced. It's curious that with all the curiosity and speculation that surround determining a baby's gender, no one has done any definitive studies to test these theories. An obstetrician friend confided that he has been conducting his own informal observations on the high and low hypothesis, but he's not about to publish any findings and "leave myself open to professional ridicule!"

Another obstetrician said the current fad among her pregnant patients is to check the baby's heartbeat, believing that the speed (fast or slow) gives an accurate determination of the baby's gender. This idea is so scientifically unsound, maintains this doctor, it's not even worth keeping track of the predictions and results.

Current tests for genetic abnormalities – amniocentesis and chorionic villus sampling – make it possible to detect if you're carrying a boy or a girl. Sonograms have become a relatively routine part of fetal monitoring during pregnancy, and a sharp-eyed technician can often spot the physical clues. Still, it's up to the parents to decide whether they really want to know beforehand. For many, especially the grandparents-to-be, the guessing game is part of the fun.

## *Don't Raise Your Hands Above Your Head, the Umbilical Cord Will Strangle the Baby.*

**NOT TRUE**

Of course, there's no way the position of your arms can possibly affect the position of the umbilical cord, which is securely enclosed, along with the baby, inside the uterus. This one was probably started by old midwives who were afraid of retribution when this tragedy occurred, preferring, instead, to pass the blame along to the poor mother. What's remarkable is that even in this century, my mother remembers being warned against doing anything that required raising her arms, like hanging curtains.

## *If You Have Heartburn When You're Pregnant, the Baby Will Have Lots of Hair.*

**NOT TRUE**

I'll never convince my mother this one isn't true. She suffered from constant heartburn throughout her pregnancy, and I was born with long, dark hair.

However, as any doctor will point out, heartburn is caused when the stomach contents back up into the esophagus. Chocolate, smoking, caffeine and fatty foods can worsen the condition, as can lying down. My mother did have to spend the last few months in bed to prevent premature labor, so perhaps that was the source of the heartburn.

In any case, this is a problem confined to the gastrointestinal system, which is separate from the heart and the uterus. So I refuse to accept guilt... my long hair was purely a coincidence!

## *If You Give in to Your Craving for Strawberries, the Baby Will Have a Strawberry Birthmark.*

**NOT TRUE**

Doctors stress that it's important for pregnant women to eat a balanced diet and that includes plenty of fruit. So if you crave strawberries, you can indulge yourself without guilt. There's no scientific basis linking any foods, eaten while pregnant, with any kind of birthmark – gynecologists say they are genetically determined.

The so-called 'strawberry' birthmark usually fades during childhood, even though it may get larger during the first year. However, disfiguring 'port wine stains', usually on the face, are birthmarks that do not fade. Fortunately, the recent development of pulsed yellow dye lasers allow treatment of port wine stains, even in newborns, without scarring.

## *You Can't Get Pregnant as Long as You're Nursing.*

**MAYBE**

With the modern choices available in contraception, it's unlikely that any mother is going to take the risk of following this particular piece of advice. If it appears to work at all, the usual explanation is that a new mother, especially when she's up in the middle of the night nursing the baby, is simply too exhausted even to consider sex.

But, surprise, surprise, surprise, this is one old wives' tale that's really true – and the reason has nothing at all to do with fatigue.

For thousands of years and even today among some cultures, breast-feeding has been an effective method of birth control, with children spaced three to four years apart. A study of pregnancy rates among Orthodox Jewish mothers, who used no artificial birth control, supported findings from underdeveloped countries.

However, what is essential is that the child be fed exclusively with breast milk – no supplemental formula and no solids – completely on demand.

Doctors explain it this way: First, when an infant nurses, there is a reflex reaction that directly inhibits the brain from releasing the hormone that allows the pituitary gland to make luteinizing hormone (LH), which is necessary to trigger ovulation. Menstruation is also delayed. Second, sucking on the breast also stimulates the pituitary gland to release the hormone *pro-*

*lactin.* High levels of prolactin, in turn, inhibit the pituitary's release of the hormone LH.

The levels of prolactin are directly related to the length of time the child nurses, as well as the frequency. Since giving supplemental bottles and/or solid food reduces the amount of time spent nursing, the levels of prolactin are also reduced, allowing ovulation.

So if you're willing to have your baby breast-feed as often as he or she is hungry, with no schedules and no supplements, you might consider asking your doctor about using this method of birth control. Of course, you may be too tired for sex, anyway.

## *Once a Caesarean, Always a Caesarean.*

**NOT TRUE**

No one knows for certain if this notion dates back to Roman times, when this procedure was named after the emperor Julius Caesar, who, as you may have already guessed, came into the world via a surgical incision. Until a few years ago, the assumption in the United States was that having once delivered by C-section, one must deliver any other infants the same way because of the risk of rupturing the uterus during the birth process. Naturally, this rule contributed to the rising number of Caesarean deliveries, now at 25 percent of all births nationwide.

In other countries, vaginal deliveries after C-sections were quite common and the rules began to change during the last decade. The obvious advantages to vaginal delivery include lower medical costs and faster recovery. Selected women who had had only one low transverse incision were allowed to attempt a 'trial of labor' for a vaginal delivery. Studies, conducted at large medical centers with routine fetal monitoring and standby surgical teams, showed successful results. It seems this OWT really has become an outdated notion, in most cases.

However, two reports in the June 1991 issue of *Obstetrics and Gynecology* raise some concerns over the increasing popularity of the practice. They estimate that one in every 100 subsequent vaginal births has resulted in uterine rupture and serious complications for mother or baby. Dr. Roy M. Pitkin summed it up in an accompanying editorial: "The message seems clear: Many women with previous Caesareans can be delivered vaginally, and thereby gain substantial advantage, but neither the decision for trial labor nor management during that labor should be arrived at in a cavalier or superficial manner."

## *You Can't Get Pregnant If You Have Sex Standing Up.*

**NOT TRUE**

When I mentioned this OWT to a friend, he recited this little ditty from his youth...

*"In days of old,*
*When knights were bold,*
*And girls were not particular,*
*They all stood up against the wall,*
*And did it perpendicular."*

Today, girls *are* particular, especially when it involves an unwanted pregnancy. Unfortunately, one out of every 10 teenagers becomes pregnant, in part due to misinformation such as this. Of course, the idea of vertical birth control is ridiculous to most adults, but it appears to be born again with each generation that enters adolescence... along with another popular misconception, pardon the pun, that "you can't get pregnant the first time."

While working on a television show with teenagers, I was quite surprised to find out how many really otherwise 'cool' teenagers place their trust in the perpendicular method. It's a belief that seems to be based on an exaggerated faith in the power of gravity, plus an ignorance of biology.

Sperm, the reasoning goes, cannot swim up, and therefore can never even make it into the vicinity of the egg, let alone hang out long enough to commit any unwanted fertilization. Ergo, safe sex.

This is only wishful thinking. Intercourse is intercourse, and those determined sperm will not simply give up. They will do what they're designed by nature to do... no matter what you do, or how you do it.

So if we're talking contraception, forget perpendicular.

# *If a Newborn Smiles, It's Only Gas & Other Parenting Proverbs*

## *When a Newborn Smiles, It's Only Gas.*

**NOT TRUE**

It's not a very charming way to describe those first smiles that parents wait for with so much expectation. But, unfortunately, gas is much more likely to generate a grimace or cry than anything resembling a smile. According to *The Growing Years*, a guide from the New York Hospital Cornell Medical Center, even "These first smiles (that appear as early as six weeks of age) are not in response to another person; they aren't social smiles, but are indications of contentment."

Not to worry, however. Babies soon begin to smile at 'anything vaguely resembling a face', an indication of the beginning of socialization. By the age of three months, babies begin to smile at their parents, which doctors point out is "a crucial development, because it indicates that the infant is responding selectively and specifically" and attachment is taking place. So go ahead and make all the silly faces you want. You may feel like an idiot, but isn't a baby's smile worth it?

I'll pass on a tip I got from Dr. T. Berry Brazelton that's sure to elicit a response from even a six-week-old. I tried it last month with a friend's baby. Just stick your tongue in and out, very slightly, making whatever sounds you can. The baby will soon start moving her tongue, smiling and making 'conversation'.

## *To Increase Milk Flow, Drink a Glass of Beer or Wine Before Nursing.*

**NOT TRUE**

Texts as far back as first century India recommend wine for the nursing mother, while many European countries have praised beer as useful in increasing the flow of milk. Now, there's no doubt that a little alcohol can relax a frazzled mother, but what effect does it have on the baby?

Some research done with nursing mothers has shown that drinking one beer, or its equivalent in other alcohol, actually has a negative effect: babies eat less, not more.

Since nearly everything a mother eats or drinks gets passed along in the breast milk, the alcohol may be sedating the baby.

Physicians strongly advise against drinking alcohol when nursing, or giving a baby alcohol in any form.

Drinking lots of fluids is more effective in producing an adequate flow of breast milk. The recommendation is two to three quarts a day of water, juice or milk.

However, would you like to know what really makes a baby nurse better? Garlic!

The American Academy of Pediatrics noted that a recent study by the Monell Chemical Senses Center found that when a mother ate garlic, one to two hours before nursing, there was an increase in the perceived intensity of the odor of their milk.

The infants stayed attached to the breast longer and ingested more milk when the milk smelled like garlic.

There's no accounting for the tastes of babies!

## *Solid Foods Will Help a Baby Sleep Through the Night.*

**NOT TRUE**

Unfortunately, the only people helped by this advice are baby food manufacturers. If it really worked, there wouldn't be so many weary new parents longing for just one unbroken night's sleep.

Until the 1980s, infants were started on solid food, usually cereal, at about four weeks of age. The seemingly defenseless child would sit, propped up in a corner of an infant seat, while you patiently spooned the food into his little mouth. Then, through a phenomenon known as the 'extrusion reflex' (a self-protective mechanism that prevents infants from swallowing anything but liquids), he would push the food back out. In some frustration you scraped it off his chin, tried again, and

maybe eventually, some food ended up inside the baby.

Not only is this aggravating process a waste of time – and baby food – but the American Academy of Pediatrics warns that young infants might have difficulty digesting and absorbing the food that does go down. Their digestive systems are really set up to handle breast milk or formula, not solids, during the early months. Another danger of starting solids too soon is that it may make a baby more prone to allergies since at this point, the intestinal tract doesn't yet have any defenses against foreign proteins.

What is the best age to start giving solids? The Academy recommends waiting until a baby is at least four months old, preferably six months.

So tell that to your mother-in-law who says you're starving her grandchild.

## *When a Baby Is Teething, It's Normal to Run a Fever.*

**NOT TRUE**

No! Teething does not cause fevers or make a baby more susceptible to colds. A fever is a sign of an infection, and should be checked out with your baby's doctor, especially if it's above 101 degrees Fahrenheit for a day or more.

Other things – drooling, a slight loss of appetite, problems sleeping, increased diaper rash and crankiness – can be blamed on teething. Dentists say the process really isn't as painful as adults think it is . . . and I'm sure no one actually remembers their teething days. But there are some ways to soothe the gums. Try a teething ring with gel that can be chilled, or gently massage the gums with a damp gauze pad. Don't rub with ice, which could damage the gum's covering. And never cut the gums to help the teeth come through . . . that is painful and can cause infection.

## *Whether the Baby's Bellybutton Is an 'Inny' or an 'Outy' Depends on How the Doctor Cut the Umbilical Cord.*

**NOT TRUE**

'Innies' and 'outies'... doesn't that bring back memories from childhood? Of course, no one ever thought or even cared about the cause, it was just something fascinating to look at and compare. In truth, the obstetrician can't be blamed either way. The position of the cut makes no difference: What does determine the shape is the same thing that shapes the baby's fingers... heredity.

My husband's grandfather had a wonderful explanation of bellybuttons, in general. He was a baker and drew his grandchildren's attention to the indentation at the center of a rye bread. "This was made," he said, "by the baker when he poked the bread to see if it was done. That's what God does, too, to tell if each new baby is ready to be born. Whether you are an inny or an outy depended on your state of doneness when you got poked." I guess you can call this one an 'old baker's tale'.

## *A Cat Will Steal a Baby's Breath.*

**NOT TRUE**

Adult cats often look like they're guilty or up to no good, which is the source of the expression "the cat that swallowed the canary." Even the most fanatic cat lover will admit that most cats seem to really enjoy making, or getting into, trouble. So, when there's a helpless little baby around, it's easy to look at the family tabby and see a real green-eyed monster prowling the nursery.

But do they really suffocate babies by 'stealing their breath'? The answer is "No." This is one time where poor cats have gotten a bum rap. The belief probably arose from the unfortunate phenomenon that used to be called 'crib death', when a perfectly healthy infant mysteriously dies while asleep. Cats love to curl up to anything warm, and it's likely that if they were found in the crib, they took the blame. The condition is now known as SIDS or Sudden Infant Death Syndrome, but there's still no definitive answer as to the cause.

Many pediatricians do agree that for other reasons, such as allergies, it may be a good idea to keep the cat out of the baby's room.

## *Don't Pick a Baby Up Every Time She Cries. She'll Get Spoiled... It's Good for a Baby to Cry, It Exercises the Lungs.*

**NOT TRUE**

This is sort of two old wives' tales in one, and the combination has created generations of howling children and guilt-ridden parents. My mother said she wore earplugs for my first few months because my screaming was so upsetting.

Fortunately, doctors and psychologists are now reassuring parents that there's no way a young baby (up to six months or so) is capable of scheming to manipulate helpless parents with the idea, "If I cry long enough and loud enough, I'll get picked up." According to respected pediatrician Dr. T. Berry Brazelton, "You can never spoil a baby with too much love and attention. Your baby is helpless, and when she needs you, she communicates in the only way she can, by crying. You teach her trust and security with lots of loving attention."

Studies have also been done on the effects of picking a baby up even when she's not crying. By six weeks of age, babies who had been carried around and cuddled an extra hour or two a day were observed to cry less. This was particularly evident during the late afternoon and evening 'fuss periods'. Crankiness and crying were actually cut in half.

## *Babies Are More Sensitive to Cold, So They Need to Be All Bundled Up.*

**NOT TRUE**

The way some parents encase their children in protective bundling, you would think they were taking a walk on the moon. These little 'astronauts' are so wrapped in layers against the cold air they are barely able to wiggle their fingers. Why all this overprotectiveness? Well, many parents truly believe that babies, especially in the first few months, are less able to cope with cold weather.

Not true, says the American Academy of Pediatrics. A 32° temperature, or below, is no colder to a baby than to an adult. So there is no reason to dress your baby any more heavily than you dress yourself. They do cite one area of exception: the baby's head. Because it's proportionally larger in terms of body area compared to an adult's, a baby can lose correspondingly more heat through his head. So, it's OK to go heavy on the hats.

The same rule about dressing applies indoors, as well. If you don't need to wear a heavy sweater, neither does your baby. Just remember, an overbundled baby won't complain, he'll simply perspire and break out in prickly heat. So common is this scenario that pediatricians say they treat more cases of prickly heat in the winter than in the summer.

If your baby is getting cold, he'll let you know by crying and turning a bluish mottled color. And, don't try to go by the feel of the child's hands or feet. They're generally a little colder than the rest of his body. Check his little tummy for a better indication of the baby's temperature.

## *If You're Not Quiet, You'll Wake the Baby.*

**NOT TRUE**

This frequent warning is often given to older children in the family and doesn't do much in the way of encouraging a positive attitude toward a new sibling. Is it really necessary? Doctors say it all depends on the baby. Even newborns are individual: Some are easily awakened by the slightest noise, while others can sleep through a Super Bowl game. I had one of each.

For most young infants, a normal level of conversation is just fine, so there's no need to whisper. A sudden noise or loud shout may cause the baby to react a little, but not fully wake up. Many desperate parents have also found that monotonous sounds of vacuums, fans, lawn mowers, drills, engines, etc., actually help put a cranky baby to sleep. The only problem is that the baby is likely to wake up as soon as you stop. I soon learned, after wearing the carpets out, it works just as well to tape the sound of a vacuum cleaner and play it as long as needed!

## *The Later a Baby's Teeth Come in, the Better They'll Be.*

**NOT TRUE**

This notion may have been started by mothers (more likely grandmothers) whose offspring were slow in cutting their first teeth. It certainly makes a good conversation stopper when someone starts bragging about how soon her grandchild's teeth appeared. Unfortunately, it is the hapless babies who innocently find themselves in endless competition – even within the same family – to be the first to turn over, teethe, crawl, walk, talk, get out of diapers, etc.

In the long run, it doesn't make any difference who's early

or late. Pediatricians keep reminding anxious parents that children develop according to their own timetables, and that includes teething. Usually, the first tooth breaks through the gum at around five to six months of age, but some infants are born with a tooth. Other children may not get that first tooth until after their first birthday. The quality of the teeth certainly isn't affected by the timing.

## *Baby Teeth Aren't Important Anyway.*

**NOT TRUE**

Now, this misconception probably originated as the perfect comeback to the above OWT. However, instead of being harmless, this belief could create serious problems. The American Academy of Pediatrics states clearly that "Baby teeth, or primary teeth, help children chew food, speak clearly and retain space for the permanent teeth that start to erupt at around five or six years of age."

The Academy stresses the importance of taking good care of baby teeth by cleaning them daily as soon as the first tooth appears (with a piece of damp gauze or cloth), and by getting proper amounts of fluoride (even before teething begins). Since the amount of fluoride in local water varies, it's best to check this out with your baby's doctor.

The most harmful thing you can do is put a baby to bed with a bottle of milk or juice – and that's exactly what many parents do. When these infants fall asleep, they can end up with a small pool of liquid in their mouths. The sugar in the milk or juice combines with bacteria to eat away at their teeth, causing what's called 'baby bottle decay'. This can also happen to a toddler who carries around a bottle of milk or juice all day and sucks on it frequently as a pacifier.

Pediatricians strongly recommend that if a baby must go to bed with a bottle, make it plain water.

## *You Have to Warm a Baby's Bottle.*

**NOT TRUE**

This OWT was most likely laid down at the beginning of the century when formulas were first developed for use in bottle feeding. Before then, a mother either breast-fed her baby or hired a wet nurse. Obviously, the reasoning went, since breast milk was served up at body temperature, bottles needed to be warmed to the same degree. Or else – as I was warned by certain well-meaning relatives – "The milk will chill the baby's tummy."

What no one took into consideration was that while breast milk is available immediately in a warmed state (one of the many advantages of breast-feeding), bottles need to be heated, tested, then usually cooled a little. All this takes time, during which you have a hungry baby screaming at the top of his lungs – especially frustrating at 3:00 a.m.

Around the same time my second child made the switch from breast to bottle, I started doing research for a book I was writing, *The Complete Guide to Preparing Baby Food*. More than a little short on time, I asked my pediatrician if it was really necessary to warm the formula. His answer was, "There's no real reason, it's just tradition." I checked some more and found that some hospitals didn't warm bottles even for newborns. As for the 'chilled tummy theory', a doctor pointed out that the milk would be warmed, anyway, during the trip down.

## *Newborns Can't See.*

**NOT TRUE**

One of the most touching moments is when your newborn infant looks intently at you with such clear eyes. Then someone says: "You know, she can't really see you."

Well, there's no need for disappointment. Research has, indeed, confirmed new mothers' convictions that babies, right from birth, can see very well, at least up to 12 inches away. Interestingly, that's the usual distance between a nursing baby and the mother's face. It's nature's way of helping the bonding process. Dr. T. Berry Brazelton has observed that infants can recognize their mothers' faces by the time they're two weeks old. For fathers, they take a little longer.

These findings also impact on the way newborns' eyes are treated. For years, it's been routine hospital procedure to use silver nitrate drops soon after birth to help prevent serious infections. However, silver nitrate is very irritating to the eye and can blur the infant's vision. The American Academy of Pediatrics and the National Society to Prevent Blindness have approved the alternative use of the antibiotics erythromycin and tetracycline. They're less irritating and more effective against chlamydia infections. Discuss this with your doctor and the hospital well before your baby's arrival.

## *Sit a Baby Up After She Eats, and She Won't Spit Up.*

**NOT TRUE**

One of the least endearing attributes of young babies is their habit of 'spitting up'. It happens just when you're least expecting it, usually when you, or the baby, are freshly dolled up in clean clothes. My younger daughter preferred waiting until my mother-in-law or some other relative was cuddling her. The usual comment was either, "You didn't burp her properly," or "Why don't you sit her up after she eats?"

Now, I knew I was doing a pretty good job as a 'burper', and I was already propping her up in an infant seat to let gravity help keep the meal down. So why was it still coming up? One answer may be she was simply eating too much, or swallowing air during feeding. However, some recent studies have shown that sitting a baby in a upright position may, instead, make the condition worse by increasing the pressure in the stomach.

The current advice is to place a baby on her stomach with her head slightly elevated by raising the head of the crib mattress (remember... no pillows!). Too late to help me, but it's certainly worth a try.

## *Children Need to Get Ten Hours Sleep a Night.*

**NOT TRUE**

Since I needed to wake up by 7:00 a.m. during elementary and junior high school, my mother simply counted back and set a 9:00 p.m. lights off bedtime. It didn't matter whether or not I was sleepy. Millions of wide-awake children are still put to bed at specific hours because "You need your sleep."

Of course, one can legitimately argue that children do need to get enough sleep, but does 'enough' really mean 10 hours? It all depends. The general advice from pediatricians is that the average six- to eight-year-old should get 12 hours a day; nine- to 12-year-olds require 10 to 11 hours; and 13- to 15-year-olds need nine to 10 hours sleep. The critical word here is 'average'.

Children, just as adults, differ in their sleep requirements. Some can manage very well, even as toddlers, on eight hours or less a night. So, instead of setting a firm time to go to sleep, doctors say parents should consider how the child wakes up. If she's wide awake and fresh in the morning, is alert in school and doesn't get tired and cranky during the day, she's probably getting enough sleep.

And just think of all the fighting that can be avoided by not forcing a child to try to sleep when she's not tired. In many families, this battle escalates into an issue that has nothing to do with sleep, but with power and control. When that happens, a child may continue to resist sleeping even when she is tired.

What if you're unlucky enough to have a child who can get by just fine with less sleep? Does that mean she can stay up until you go to sleep? Not necessarily. If you'd like a little peace, quiet and free time at night – and what parent doesn't – you can still set a specific 'bedtime'. A child can read, play, sing, or anything she enjoys, so long as she's ready for bed and, preferably, in her room.

## *Never Take a Sick Child Outside.*

**NOT TRUE**

This dictum passed into history along with doctors' house calls, and every mother nowadays knows it just isn't true. However, I still recall how shocked and indignant I was when the nurse told me to bring my three-month-old daughter (running a 102° fever) into the office. And in December, no less! I know I never went out, even in the summer, if I was running even the slightest fever.

Besides being convenient for the doctor, there is an advantage in your going to the doctor's office. Keep in mind it's the best place to do a proper examination and begin any necessary treatment. Obviously, there's no harm in taking a sick infant or child (dressed properly) outside even if it's for other reasons than going to the doctor.

# *Don't Store Food in Open Cans & Other Advice to Chew On*

## *Don't Store Food in Open Cans; It Will Spoil.*

**NOT TRUE**

I've heard this admonition all my life, but never had an explanation that made sense. After all, the inside of the can was sterilized before it was opened, so why not just cover the can and put it in the fridge? You save time and extra containers, which you don't sterilize, anyway. Unless the can got pushed to the back of the shelf and sat there for months, becoming a mold factory, I've never had open canned food spoil. Still, the warning has made enough of an impression so that I feel slightly uneasy whenever I ignore it.

To get to the bottom of whether or not this really is an OWT, I went to the top source I could think of, the U.S. Department of Agriculture, and talked with the Supervisory Home Economist, Lois H. Fulton, M.S., R.D. She confirmed my heretical belief that storing food in the original can in the fridge does not cause it to spoil faster.

On the other hand, she did not recommend the

practice. Why? Because the food is more likely to pick up an off-flavor from the can, even if it's covered. Now that's something that I can understand. In the recent book *Safe Food, The Center for Science in the Public Interest* (CSPI) offers another reason for transferring food to another container. The authors point out that if lead solder was used in the seams of the can, the oxygen would help the lead dissolve and leach into the food, especially if it's acidic like tomatoes or citrus juice.

Lead, even in small amounts, poses a real danger because it builds up in the body. And it can leach into food even if the can is unopened. Fortunately, lead-soldered cans are becoming rare in the U.S., but they are fairly common in imported foods, like mushrooms, fruits, fish, tomatoes, artichokes and water chestnuts. CSPI recommends that you use only seamless cans or those with welded seams. You can usually tell if a seam is soldered by running your finger down the seam and checking for unevenness through the label.

## *Breakfast Is the Most Important Meal of the Day.*

**TRUE**

My generation certainly grew up hearing, and believing, in this statement. Which doesn't stop most of us from rushing out in the morning fortified with only a cup of coffee and toast. However, in an estimated 40 percent of American families there isn't even an adult present in the kitchen to urge children to finish their breakfast. So, more children skip breakfast than any other meal. This is one adage that may end with this generation, unfortunately.

While no one has proven conclusively that breakfast is the most important meal of the day, it's at least of equal importance with lunch and dinner. Nutritionists warn that your body burns the energy from food within four hours. Although you may use up less energy while you sleep, it's a long time until morning and you still wake up with the need for lots more fuel.

Some studies have shown that children who skip breakfast don't do as well in school. Besides lack of energy, we all know how tough it is to concentrate when your stomach's rumbling and you're counting hours until lunch.

In addition, a recent Canadian study suggests that skipping breakfast may increase the chance of a heart attack. It's been known that the incidence of heart attacks is highest in the first few hours after waking. According to the study, the blood protein (beta thromboglobulin), which increases as blood cells prime themselves for clotting, averaged nearly three times higher in people who did not eat breakfast.

So, there's no doubt the importance of breakfast is more than just an old wives' tale. The problem comes in following the advice: How do you find time to make a proper meal and then make time to eat it?

The American Health Association recommends that breakfast should supply at least one-fourth of the daily food needs. And it's important to include a variety of foods to supply energy until the next meal. Carbohydrates (bread, for example) can be digested in as little as 30 minutes; however protein (eggs, milk, meat, cheese) lasts longer, and can help you make it to lunchtime.

Many nutritionists say one answer is in expanding the common idea of what constitutes breakfast. Foods like pizza, peanut butter and jelly sandwiches, hearty soups and fruit milk shakes are all perfectly acceptable and are more likely to be eaten by children. As for the question of preparation time, or lack of it, why not try recycling leftovers from the previous dinner. If, like me, you wake up in the morning barely capable of pouring cereal into a bowl, you can always spend a few minutes at night making a breakfast that only needs a quick nuking in the microwave, or can be eaten cold. Ever try leftover pizza right from the fridge? Not bad!

## *Carrots Are Good for Your Eyesight.*

**TRUE**

After a visit with her grandmother, our younger daughter suddenly refused to eat carrots. Why? Bethany emphatically explained, "Nana said they would give me pointy eyes!" Upon further questioning, we finally figured out Nana had readily told her carrots would give her 'sharp' eyes. An easy misunderstanding for a three-year-old.

We reassured her, and confirmed that, yes, eating up all her carrots would help her have good eyesight. Were we really just perpetuating an old wives' tale? Not exactly.

Vitamin A is necessary for maintaining normal epithelial tissue, which includes the cornea and conjunctiva of the eyes. It's also essential in helping the eye adjust efficiently to changes in the intensity of light, like going outside on a sunny day. A deficiency in this vitamin can cause eye problems, including burning, itching and inflamed eyes. Of course, there are many more likely causes.

So vitamin A is important for your eyes, and carrots are, indeed, an excellent source of carotene, a form of this vitamin. Other dark yellow vegetables (sweet potatoes, melons) and dark green vegetables (spinach, parsley, etc.) also contain high amounts of carotene.

Another form of vitamin A is retinol, which can be obtained from liver, eggs, whole milk and cheese. It's obvious that by eating a varied diet, not just carrots, children and adults will get enough vitamin A.

And although vitamin A is necessary, it doesn't mean you should consume very large amounts or take supplements. Since this is a fat soluble vitamin, excess amounts are stored in the body and can reach harmful levels. Too high a dosage of vitamin A has been implicated in some eye disorders and other health problems.

The bottom line: A moderate amount of carrots is essential for healthy eyes, but carrots or any other vitamin A food won't ensure 20/20 eyesight. I've been eating up all my carrots for years and I still need to wear glasses.

## *Mayonnaise Makes Food Spoil Faster.*

**NOT TRUE**

For many kids, mayonnaise can transform what they consider 'yuck' into an edible sandwich. But every time my mother caught me spreading it on my children's school lunches, she warned... "You know, those sandwiches won't be in a refrigerator and the mayonnaise can make them spoil faster." I used it, anyway, since everyone seemed to survive, but I always felt slightly guilty that I was, indeed, increasing the risk of food poisoning.

It wasn't until years later, when I was researching a book, that I came across the statement that the acid (lemon juice or vinegar) in mayonnaise actually helps delay the growth of harmful bacteria and spoilage. I confirmed this revelation with nutritionists, doctors and the U.S. Department of Agriculture. They did recommend the use of commercial mayo over the homemade type for two reasons: The acid content is higher and it's made with pasteurized eggs, instead of raw eggs, which often carry salmonella bacteria.

Even though this proved to be a real old wives' tale, it doesn't mean you should leave food unrefrigerated for hours, with or without mayo. All food contains bacteria and can spoil given enough time. But the mayo isn't the culprit. Of course, I'll never convince my mother and I still don't like mayonnaise on sandwiches.

## *Fertilized Eggs Are More Nutritious.*

**NOT TRUE**

Health food stores often make this claim, but the embryo in a fertilized egg is so small that it doesn't add any significant nutritional value to the egg.

Another common misconception is that a blood spot in the yolk means it's fertilized. No way. According to the American Egg Board, a blood spot is caused by the rupture of a blood vessel on the yolk's surface while the egg was being formed, or by a similar accident as the membrane travels down the reproductive tract. Should you toss it or cook it? These blood spots are really harmless, so don't even bother removing them. Unless you're like me – irrationally squeamish.

Here are a few more egg-cellent facts from the Egg Board about the new old wives' tales.

## *Brown Eggs Are More Nutritious Than White Eggs.*

**NOT TRUE**

Not so. The color of the shell has nothing to do with nutrition or flavor. It simply depends on which variety of hen is laying the eggs.

## *Raw Eggs Are More Nutritious Than Cooked Eggs.*

**NOT TRUE**

Absolutely not! However, they are more dangerous because a high percentage of eggs are contaminated by the bacteria that causes salmonella poisoning. Fortunately, it's destroyed by thorough cooking. Doctors advise against eating any raw or underdone eggs. No more sunnyside up, over easy, or loosely scrambled. That also eliminates drinking a raw egg in a glass of tomato juice as a hangover cure – ugh! (As we found earlier it's not such a great idea anyway.)

## *Don't Eat Between Meals; You'll Spoil Your Appetite.*

**NOT TRUE**

In terms of childhood aggravation and frustration, this all too familiar warning ranks right up there with "Don't Read in Dim Light" and "Don't go Swimming After Eating." And it's just as unfounded!

To convince doubting mothers (and grandmothers), I went to the highest authority – the American Academy of Pediatrics – who sent me their guide *Right From the Start: ABCs of Good Nutrition*. It clearly states, "Snacking makes up an important part of childhood nutrition. Children must eat frequently because they have high energy needs." They advise two or three healthful snacks a day, between meals!

So what if a child eats less at dinner? It doesn't mean he 'spoiled his appetite', only that he's not ravenous because he wasn't allowed food during the long stretch between lunch and dinner. Actually, it's mainly an American custom to save the largest meal for the last. In Europe and many other areas, the midday meal is usually the most elaborate and supplies energy needed for the rest of the active day.

The key word is healthful – meaning full of nutrition, not full of fat and sugar, like potato chips and candy. Sure, these junk foods may supply energy, but no nutrition. Some good snacks are fresh fruits, raw vegetables, bagels, graham crackers, string cheese, turkey slices, peanut butter, pizza – anything you'd normally serve at meals, just in smaller amounts.

When you think about it, the practice of eating three meals a day is really designed more for adult convenience than children's needs. And doctors say it's a smart idea for adults to also eat smaller amounts, more frequently. There's even a new word that suppresses any leftover guilt from getting caught with your hand in the cookie jar. Instead of snacking, you can now say you're 'grazing'.

## *Storing Onions With Potatoes Will Make Them Sprout.*

**NOT TRUE**

A friend came up with this OWT, which seemed to explain why the onions and potatoes I usually stored together under the sink would sprout in record time. Once again, I checked with Lois H. Fulton, Supervisory Home Economist with the U.S. Department of Agriculture.

She said she didn't know any reason why storing these vegetables together would cause sprouting, but they shouldn't be stored together, anyway. Why? Because mature onions should be kept at room temperature, or slightly cooler, in loosely woven or open mesh containers. However, potatoes should be stored in a dark dry place with good ventilation, at a temperature of about 45 to 50 degrees Fahrenheit. High temperatures will speed up the sprouting process.

That's certainly a logical explanation for the garden that's usually growing in my under-sink cabinet. It was too humid for the onions, and too hot and humid for the potatoes.

## *Potatoes Are Fattening.*

**NOT TRUE**

These days, any informed dieter worth his fat knows very well this concept isn't true. One large potato contains 130 calories, no more than a serving of cottage cheese or tuna fish. Plus, it's free of fat and cholesterol, so long as you leave off the butter, sour cream, cheddar cheese and gravy!

## *Yams and Sweet Potatoes Are the Same Vegetables.*

**NOT TRUE**

This is probably a relatively modern misconception, and one that seems to be very common. Back in the old days, when most people grew their own vegetables, I'm sure yams were very seldom confused with sweet potatoes. But is it really important to know they're completely different? The answer is "yes", because there's a real difference in nutritional value between the two of them.

*Nutrition Action*, CSPI's health newsletter, points out that compared to yams, the orange-colored sweet potatoes are in the four-star category, especially when it comes to beta carotene (a form of vitamin A). One medium sweet potato provides more than four times the U.S. Recommended Daily Allowance, while the poor pale yam contains none.

Many grocery clerks don't know the difference and the names are often used interchangeably. So ignore the signs over the bin, and try to remember that yams are longer and more cylindrical, with rough, scaly brownish or tan skin. Sweet potatoes are stubbier, and have tapered ends and smooth, thin skin that can range from orange to purple. You can rummage around until you find a tuber with a little skin scraped off. If the flesh is orange (which means beta carotene), then you have a sweet potato.

As for canned goods, I just checked the label on a popular brand I had on my shelf. In large letters, it clearly says 'Yams'. In smaller letters just below, it says 'Sweet Potatoes'. However, the list of ingredients on the side of the can does not list yams, only sweet potatoes, so there you have it, that's the final word. I'm not sure if the manufacturer is confused, or just wants to cover all the bases.

If you're still confused, don't worry. Most of the fresh 'yams' sold in the United States are really sweet potatoes, and likewise for canned 'yams'.

## *Cottage Cheese Is a Good Source of Calcium.*

**NOT TRUE**

I've written a lot about nutrition, but the answer to this one surprised me. Compared to other dairy products, cottage cheese is actually a poor source of calcium. During production, it loses 50 to 70 percent of the calcium initially present in the milk. Skim milk, non-fat yogurt and Swiss cheese contain much higher amounts of calcium. As for non-dairy sources, broccoli, spinach, salmon and sardines are high in calcium. This mineral is important because it helps prevent osteoporosis or 'brittle bones'.

## *Brown Sugar, Raw Sugar, Molasses and Honey Are Healthier Than Refined White Sugar.*

**NOT TRUE**

This is a new old wives' tale created in the health-conscious 1960s and 70s. For hundreds of years, wives never had a problem with white and refined sugar, basically because it was never available. They made do quite nicely with maple syrup, honey, molasses and raw cane or beet sugar when that was handy. But are these sweeteners really better for you than white sugar?

Nutritionists all agree there is no significant amount of vitamins or minerals in any of these alternative sweeteners. So you can't ease your guilty sweet tooth with the justification that you're using 'health foods'. Honey has an additional problem in that it can cause the botulism toxin to grow in the intestinal tracts of infants. It should never be given to children under one year old.

These days, foods contain many other forms of sugar, and these may be hyped to seem as if they're more nutritious, but they aren't. Sucrose, fructose, high fructose corn syrup and corn sweeteners are the most common ones you see on labels.

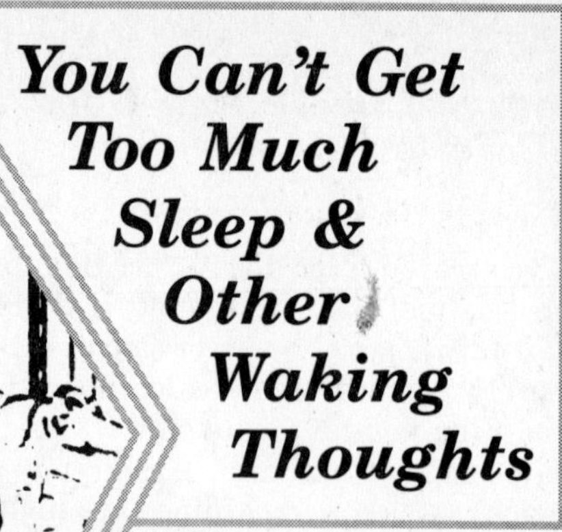

# *You Can't Get Too Much Sleep & Other Waking Thoughts*

### *You Can't Get Too Much Sleep.*

**NOT TRUE**

There's no benefit in getting more sleep than you need, and that varies among individuals. Yet, people can get into the habit of sleeping a specific number of hours, or they stay in bed because 'it's good for you'. Of course, there's no harm, but if you'd like a little more time during the day, try cutting back an hour of sleep for a few nights and see how you feel.

If it's of any help, the Better Sleep Council reveals that the average person sleeps seven and a half hours each night. And the average number of hours a person spends asleep during a lifetime is a whopping 220,000!

## *You Can't Catch Up on Sleep.*

**NOT TRUE**

Yes, you can usually catch up with one good long sleep, even if you've been burning the midnight oil for several nights. And don't bother keeping count of hours of lost sleep – you don't have to make up every hour.

## *You Need Less Sleep as You Get Older.*

**NOT TRUE**

Not necessarily. Adults generally need less sleep than children; however, the amount doesn't just continue decreasing with age. Older people, especially men, may wake up with frequent trips to the bathroom and then have difficulty in going back to sleep. It's also normal for sleep patterns to change as you get older, and many people find themselves wide awake at 5:00 a.m. If you tend to get tired during the day, doctors advise adjusting to the new patterns by going to bed earlier or taking a nap during the day. Sleeping pills are not the answer.

## *A Nap Just Leaves You Feeling Groggy.*

**NOT TRUE**

Not according to experts on sleep and attentiveness. They say that an afternoon nap can refresh a person, especially if he or she has a stressful job. It could help reduce errors, at the same time increasing creativity and productivity. Research shows that people have natural circadian (24-hour) cycles that encourage us to sleep twice a day: in the middle of the night and the middle of the afternoon.

Psychologist Ernest Lawrence Rossi goes further in his focus on the body's ultradian (less than 24-hour) rhythms which occur every 90 minutes. His recommendation: 20-minute breaks every 1½ hours to improve work performance, mood and physical well-being. Tell that to your boss or teacher!

## *One Hour's Sleep Before Midnight Is Worth Two After.*

**NOT TRUE**

False again. This old wives' tale was probably invented by mothers who couldn't wait to pack their teenagers off to bed.

## *A Little Warm Milk Will Help You Go to Sleep.*

**TRUE**

How many movies and plays have you seen in which someone offers the unsuspecting heroine 'a nice cup of warm milk to help you sleep better'? Too often, the milk contains a sinister white powder that insures the drinker sleeps very soundly, indeed, likely to be discovered dead in the morning, with the telltale cup smashed on the floor.

Assuming you trust the preparer and the warm milk is safe to drink, does it actually promote sleep? Or is this just an old wives' tale which mystery writers have found very convenient?

The truth is that milk can increase your chances of drifting easily off to sleep. It's rich in calcium, which helps relax muscles, and is also a source of tryptophan, a protein that enables the brain to produce serotonin. This chemical, in turn, helps switch on the brain's sleep centers.

If you're like me, and can't stand the thought of warm milk, you'll be happy to know that cold milk works just as well. Though my husband insists that, warm or cold, the milk really needs a cookie to be effective.

# *If a Dog's Nose Is Hot and Dry, It Means He's Sick & Other Clues to the Secret Lives of Pets*

## *If a Dog's Nose Is Hot and Dry, He's Sick.*

**NOT TRUE**

We thought this rule of thumb was so obviously true that it wasn't even worth covering. However, the woman at Animals By Choice asked if we were going to say anything about the dog's nose.

Why? We wondered. Because, she said, it was one of the most flagrant examples of a commonly accepted fact that was dead wrong. A dry nose indicates nothing at all about a dog's health. It is only a sign that the dog has been inactive for a period. He has either been sleeping or resting.

The lesson from that is not to take anything for granted, no matter how obviously true, or false. Each common notion must be checked out. And that's why we asked this obvious question...

## *Barking Dogs Don't Bite.*

**NOT TRUE**

Some do, some don't.

According to the people at the SPCA of Westchester County in New York, you believe this one at your own risk.

Barking dogs can and do bite, before and after they bark.

## *If a Dog's Tail Is Wagging, She Is Friendly.*

**MAYBE**

The dog that's barking at you may also be wagging his tail at the same time. Does this mean he won't bite?

A spokesperson at Animals By Choice, a nonprofit organization in Westchester County in New York, said that your chances of safely approaching a barking dog whose tail is wagging are pretty good. Tail wagging usually means the dog is happy. But this is not 100 percent certain; people have been known to be bitten by dogs who were wagging their tails.

# *The Full Moon Makes People Crazy & Other Weather Reports*

## *Moon Myths . . . Tides, Sex, Sanity and the Weather*

On the first evening after the dawn of civilization, primitive man looked up and there it was: the moon.

Fortunately, we don't really have to imagine what he or she thought of this nearest celestial neighbor . . . legends, religions, folklore and years of study have been documented and chronicled and we have enough information available for a life's work.

For instance, we know that it didn't take early man very long to discover a correlation between the rising of the moon and the local tidal ebb and flow. And it was this power that placed the moon into the hierarchy of early religions, along with the sun, the wind, the rains and snows, and the seasons.

We will probably never know when man first noticed the hounds baying at (or in sync with) the full moon, or that his own romantic interests seemed to be aroused at the same time. However, there was enough connection between the rising of the moon and offbeat behavior for the words 'lunacy' and 'lunatic' to enter our vocabulary, *luna* being the Latin word for 'moon'.

Today, and for recent history, we understand that the moon's 'power' is its gravity, or gravitational pull. We also understand that the moon moves around the earth in an elliptical orbit, bringing it nearer on a predictable timetable, and changing the way it appears to us.

Since the moon is smaller than the Earth, its gravitational pull is less and it cannot move the Earth itself (there is some debate on this) very much. But it can affect things on the Earth, and what it does and does not affect defines the validity of some very familiar old wives' tales.

## *The Moon Governs Tides.*

**TRUE**

This is an unalterable fact, so much so it cannot really be deemed an OWT. We only include it because it seems to be the proof that other OWTs are true. For an explanation of this phenomena we turned to a very lucid piece of writing by Patrick Moore, director of the Lunar Section of the British Astronomical Association, and a prolific writer and lecturer. In his book *New Guide to the Moon*, Mr. Moore explains the rather complicated variations of tides and lunar proximity, and although quite fascinating, it's too involved to get into here. But the very simple explanation is that the water heaps up as the moon passes near the various parts of the Earth, almost like a wave following a magnet.

The odd thing is that the water also heaps up on the opposite side of the Earth at the same time. This is explained as either the result of the Earth being pulled away from the water by the moon's gravity, or the result of a total absence of gravitational pull from the moon on that side of the Earth. According to Mr. Moore, this is still under debate.

## *The Full Moon Makes People Crazy.*

**NOT TRUE**

Despite our words lunatic and lunacy, the word seems to be that this is simply not true. Patrick Moore went to considerable trouble to research this and found that the moon had no discernible affect on the behavior of human beings, nor any other land-based creature. But Mr. Moore admits to a slight amount of prejudice, since he spends a lot of time looking at the moon and doesn't really want to think his sanity has been affected.

Because of this, we turned to the American Museum Hayden Planetarium in New York, to see if there was any later thinking on the subject. After all, human beings are about two-thirds water, so it would seem to be a logical assumption. Suzanne Chippendale, the planetarium's writer and producer, was happy to back Moore up. When asked why the moon's gravity can affect tides and not people, she explained that people were simply too small to be affected. In other words, there has to be considerable size and mass for all that gravity to matter.

So how did all this 'lunacy' business start? There had to be some aberration connected with the moon. Ms. Chippendale has a rational response to that, too. It is simply the light from the full moon. The fact is that more light, especially in the days before we knew how to make our own light in ample quantities, caused changes in the behavior of all creatures, both on land and in the sea. People could be active under a full moon in a way they could not when there was little or no moonlight, and the same holds true for animals and fish who can use the extra light to find food. Which brings us to the next moon-related OWT . . .

## *We Are More Romantic, and Conceive More Babies During a Full Moon.*

**NOT TRUE**

"By the Light of the Silvery Moon," etc., says it all, according to Ms. Chippendale. Full moons are romantic because they are pretty and because of the light they deliver. Cuddling in the moonlight is more fun in the same way that it's nicer to cuddle in a rose garden than on a city street, but has nothing whatsoever to do with the gravitational pull of the moon.

Ms. Chippendale and Mr. Moore also agree on the 'statistics' regarding conception during a full moon. They cite something that is the bane of all research: "A search for coincidences will always reveal them." In other words, it is easy to find proof that there is an increase in conception during a full moon, if you look for it. However, further research will reveal other jumps in conception rate that have no relation at all to a full moon. Both instances prove nothing.

## *A Ring Around the Moon Means Rain.*

**TRUE**

The soft and often beautiful 'haloes' we sometimes see around the moon can, indeed, be precursors of rain. Again, we refer to the writing of Patrick Moore, who informs us that these rings are caused by the moonlight shining through ice crystals hovering at around 20,000 feet. These ice crystals are part of a cloud called cirrostratus, known to mariners as 'mares' tails'. They are a high, wispy cloud that is very often a sign of approaching bad weather.

The moon can also look 'watery' because it is seen through a lower and denser cloud, and this, too, can mean a soggy day is coming.

## *Don't Stand Under a Tree in a Thunderstorm.*

**TRUE**

In case you're thinking, "Of course, that's not an old wives' tale, it's absolutely true" – you're absolutely right! But judging from the speed with which most people run for shelter under the nearest tree as soon as the skies open, they either haven't heard this warning or think of it as just another old wives' tale. Unfortunately, thousands of people are injured each year by lightning.

The National Safety Council clearly explains: "Trees are tall and therefore attract lightning. Since wood is not a good conductor, an electrical current may jump from a tree to a nearby person before touching the ground." They recommend that if you are in a wooded area when a storm hits, stay at least six feet from any tree.

It can also be dangerous to be on hilltops and in open areas such as golf courses, soccer fields and baseball diamonds – especially if you're holding metal objects like golf clubs, baseball bats, fishing poles, tennis rackets, or riding a bike, moped, motorcycle, farm vehicle, etc. These all make wonderful lightning rods, so get rid of them, or get off them immediately. If you are caught in the open, the Council's advice is to "crouch low to the ground, with your hands on your knees." Don't lie flat on the ground because that increases your chances of being affected by electrical currents when the ground is struck. Sure, you'll be wet and uncomfortable, but alive.

The best idea is to get in the habit of keeping a 'weather eye' when the skies are threatening. In almost all cases, you can see the towering thunder storm cloud formation approaching and occasional lightning flashes at least half an hour in advance, plenty of time to take shelter. Even when darkness makes it hard to see the sky, keep in mind that light travels much faster than sound. It is possible to estimate the distance in miles; just count the number of seconds between the lightning flash and the accompanying thunderclap, then divide by five. If the interval between seeing the flash and hearing the thunder becomes noticeably smaller, then the storm is moving toward you.

The Safety Council also points out: "The most dangerous time to be caught outdoors is just before the storm, when dark clouds appear and your hair feels as if it's standing on end. You're being set up as a perfect lightning rod."

Talk about stupidity, I vividly remember one evening sailboat race. For over half an hour, countless eyes in over 30 boats observed dark clouds, thunder and sharply defined lightning bolts come closer and closer. But everyone hung in, with spinnakers flying, trying to reach the finish line before the storm. For once, it was lucky we weren't in the lead – that boat took a direct hit. Fortunately, most larger sailboats are grounded to handle lightning, and the only real damage was to all the electrical instruments.

Of course, water is normally a great conductor of electricity and the last place to be in a storm; that's why it's 'out of the pool' at the first clap of thunder. Where is it safe? The Council says a metal top car or bus, with closed windows, because the vehicle's frame will deflect the charge to the ground. The best place to take shelter is a large, lightning-protected or steel-framed building. However, since an estimated 18,000 homes in the

U.S. are struck by lightning each year, here's some advice if you're at home during a storm.

- Unplug the TV set because the charge can travel down the antenna and cause the set to explode.
- Don't use the telephone or electrical appliances because lightning can also travel through phone lines and electrical wiring, giving a serious shock to anyone touching the receiver or appliance.

Now I realize this may be more than you ever wanted to know about lightning, but you never know when it may come in handy. At least you'll be able to recognize any real old wives' tales about electrical storms.

## *The Full Moon Swallows the Clouds.*

**NOT TRUE**

Here is a weather-related old country adage that springs from the observed phenomena of the sky always clearing when a full moon rises. Although quite often true, this phenomena has more to do with the sun than the moon, as the sun can cause weather changes and it is generally believed that the moon does not. Moonrise occurs as the sun sets, and any clearing activity in the sky has to do with the setting sun and not the rising full moon.

# *No Pain, No Gain & Other Rumors of the Workout Room*

More people are running, jogging, lifting and doing all kinds of exercises than ever before. Dieting and fitness routines are 'in' and it's not surprising a new crop of OWTs have sprung up in the past few years. Like...

## *No Pain, No Gain.*

**NOT TRUE**

They shout it at you from the TV screens, and in the gyms, and if you're anything like me, you want to shout back, "Pain? No way!" More of an Old Trainers' Tale than an Old Wives' Tale, it's a tale that has come to be accepted as gospel truth in the last few years. It is also why more than half the population of the United States still does not really exercise. We feel guilty, of course, but who, in their right mind, likes pain?

Drs. Peter and Lorna Francis (both Ph.D.s) have written a book called *If It Hurts, Don't Do It*. Exactly my sentiments. But, if we 'don't do it' when it hurts, will we derive any benefit? Is there gain without pain?

The answer is not a simple, straightforward yes or no. It really depends on what exercises you are doing and why you are doing them.

You should exercise for health. It's a good idea to exercise for fitness. And you can exercise for strength and performance, too. Three different reasons demanding three different approaches, and two different answers to the no pain, no gain debate.

When exercising for health, a moderate program is in order. These are exercises that help you lose and maintain weight; reduce the risk of heart problems through aerobic activities such as walking and swimming; maintain flexibility; and induce relaxation. When engaging in a program like this there is no reason at all to do anything that causes discomfort, shortness of breath or pain. Just performing these activities at a comfortable level will bring about improvements.

Exercising for fitness requires more effort, more cardiovascular activity, more dedication, and should include stretching, aerobic training, and a program for building strength. Here again, there is no need to endure pain to achieve gain. It's OK to try to push past a little fatigue, but when your tired arms and legs start shaking uncontrollably, it's time to ease up. All of the above activities can be extremely beneficial without putting undue strain on your joints, ligaments and cardiovascular system. Most important, by exercising within these painless guidelines, there will be gain. Your stamina and ability will steadily improve if you stick to your program. Even the strength training you incorporate into the program does not require pain to achieve results.

For those people who train for performance, the answer is different. These are people who are interested in training for a specific sport, or simply building a very muscular body. Experts seem to agree that when it comes to developing specific muscles, there is a benefit from the fatigue one feels as one reaches and pushes capacity. However, the pain or 'burn' must still be mild and confined to the muscle itself. Great care must be taken not to tax the ligaments, the skeletal structure or the cardiovascular system that supports those muscles. Research shows that injury rates are higher among the very fit; ignoring pain can almost guarantee an injury.

One of the most awful moments of my television sports viewing career occurred when I saw a weight lifter's leg snap under the weight he had hoisted. His muscular strength had achieved a capacity his skeleton could not support.

So, for serious trainers, mild fatigue pain in the muscle itself can deliver gain, but for the rest of us it is not necessary to exercise to the point of pain to receive the benefit. Everyone who exercises, at any level, should keep in mind that pain is nature's way of warning us that we are abusing our bodies.

## *Muscle Weighs More Than Fat.*

**TRUE**

Among the explanations heard when the scale doesn't budge or even creeps upward, this theory is the 'heavyweight' champ, just edging out 'heavy bones'. People say they exercise and exercise but because the muscle they are building weighs more than the fat they are replacing, their weight remains constant. Are they right? Perhaps this is not the whole story.

Partially because he wanted to know, and partially to get me to let up on him at dinnertime, my husband asked Diane, a very knowledgeable trainer at his gym, what she knew about the subject.

"It's like the old question of a pound of bricks or a pound of feathers," she answered. "Muscle is muscle and fat is fat and a pound of each is a pound of each." But... Here's the difference.

Muscle is more dense and will weigh more than an equal amount of fat, just like a brick will weigh more than a stack of

feathers the same size as the brick. But how does that all relate to weight loss? Will a person who is exercising and building muscle actually gain weight? The answer is in the calorie intake.

Let's compare two people taking in 2,000 calories per day, one working out, the other not. The person working out will burn most of the calories while building muscle, so that person will lose weight. The calories taken in, but not used, by the sedentary individual will build fat.

However, if the person who is working out increases his or her intake of calories, then there will be less and less weight loss as they bulk up. They will be building muscle but not burning enough calories, and those extra calories turn to fat. This is a general rule and, naturally, the two different bodies react to the rule at different rates.

## *When You Stop Exercising, Muscle Turns to Fat.*

**NOT TRUE**

This popular myth is perpetuated by the apparent frequency of gigantic football players and weight lifters turning into 'The Blob' when their careers end.

Again, muscle is muscle and fat is fat. They are different tissues, and one cannot turn into the other. The sloppy ex-athlete is simply continuing, or increasing, his or her intake of calories without burning them off with exercise, thereby adding fat to the body.

The appearance of muscle turning into fat, and vice versa, is, however, another story and brings us to the next OWT...

## *You Can Get Rid of Cellulite.*

**NOT TRUE**

Some French marketing genius, no doubt lounging on the beach in Cannes, sipping a glass of wine and enjoying a zesty bowl of spaghetti bolognese, was musing on his lack of opportunities. Suddenly, his experienced eye noticed something... something both ugly and beautiful at the same time. Leaping from his chair, and knocking the spaghetti and wine onto his white linen trousers, he screamed the French word for 'Eureka!' Looking, as Frenchmen sometimes do, at the thighs and backsides of hundreds of women, he had discovered, tucked beneath their suntanned skins, a mother lode of pure gold.

He had discovered what would become known as cellulite, one of the great myths of the 20th century, or an 'Old Advertisers' Tale'.

We don't know for sure that it happened that way, but it could have. What we do know is that this designation and labeling of a purely natural phenomenon, occurring most often in women, gave birth not only to a billion dollar industry, but a complete pseudo science, as well.

In *The Skin Book*, the authors Drs. Arnold W. Klein and James H. Steinberg state clearly that "cellulite is an imaginary condition"... there's no such thing as cellulite itself. They go on to say that "studies have shown that 'cellulite' is not actually a disease, but merely an anatomically normal irregularity, simply a result of the fact that fat deposits in women's legs are different from fat deposits in men's legs." Men have crisscrossing connective tissue strands that keep the fat from forming in large chambers as it does in women.

Since their book came out 10 years ago, this perfectly normal condition has spawned a gigantic number of institutions, clinics, 'professionals', and folklore of technical expertise. Products by the hundreds, featuring miracle drugs, enzymes, etc., have been developed to be taken, injected and rubbed into the 'affected areas'. Recommendations include massaging to break up the cellulite, opening the blood vessels beneath the skin, getting rid of salt, staying off coffee and cigarettes, eliminating specific foods, deep breathing, stress management, etc., etc., etc.

Much of this advice will contribute to improving one's general health, but won't help to get rid of those ugly dimples – which women are obviously desperate to do – myself included.

So is there any hope? Drs. Klein and Steinberg confirm the accepted medical recommendation that only exercise and weight loss may help in reducing these fat deposits, and can forestall them if you begin early enough – after all, female athletes don't have cellulite.